Pasteur and the
Invisible Giants

PASTEUR
and the
Invisible Giants

By Edward F. Dolan, Jr.

DODD, MEAD & COMPANY

New York

For Rose,

Timothy and Wendy

Contents

Pasteur and the
Invisible Giants

A Career Begins

It was a beautiful morning, but Louis Pasteur had no eyes for it. He didn't even notice how the sunlight made a vast mirror of Paris streets still wet from last night's shower. On this autumn day in 1846, the young chemist walked with his head down and a puzzled frown darkening his face. He seemed to have forgotten entirely that his best friend, Charles Chappuis, was striding along beside him.

On the Rue d'Ulm, they stopped before the ancient brick building in which hundreds of young Frenchmen were trained for the teaching profession—the École Normale. As Louis stared up at the school front, his frown deepened. Thick glasses made pinpoints of sharp blue eyes.

"I just don't understand it," he said to his friend Charles. "What can he want?"

Charles, as lean as Louis was stocky, grinned and suggested, "Why don't you go inside and find out?"

But Louis remained where he was. He dug into his trouser pocket and extracted the now crumpled sheet of paper that a messenger had delivered to his room at Monsieur Barbet's School last night.

He glimpsed the expression of impatience that flicked across Charles' face at the sight of that paper, and he felt a tiny thrust of guilt. Chappuis had come to Paris just yesterday to spend a brief holiday with his old school friend, and, bored with his life as a teacher in a distant, provincial town, had anticipated a round of the theaters and restaurants he remembered so fondly from student days. And how have I entertained him thus far? Louis asked himself. He has had to watch me read this note a hundred times over.

Ah, well, once more won't hurt. He lifted the paper to his stubby nose and read to himself: "Please come to my laboratory at ten in the morning. I have something to tell you that I think will be of great interest to you."

The note was signed by one of Louis' professors, the world-famous chemist, Antoine Balard.

"I don't see why he couldn't want you to help him with an experiment," Charles said a bit irritably. Last night he had insisted that this was entirely possible—but Louis' modesty wouldn't hear of it.

Louis shook his head. Straight dark hair fell across a prominent forehead. "But why should he?" Louis asked perplexedly. "He's an outstanding chemist, and I'm . . ."

"I know. You're just a student," Charles mocked, his impatience quite apparent now. He seemed about to repeat all the things he had said last night when the note had first arrived: that Louis was a very advanced student, that he had just been graduated from the École Normale and was now a licensed teacher at work on his Doctor of Science degree, that he knew chemistry up and down and that it was not impossible that Balard should need his help. Instead, he now merely smiled and said, "You think too little of yourself, Louis. But have it your own way. Now go inside. I'll wait for you here."

Louis nodded, squared his shoulders, and ascended the steps to the building entrance.

"Louis—" Charles called.

"Yes?"

"Good luck. I feel something fine is going to happen."

Louis waved his gratitude. "Thank you."

Turning away from his friend, Louis saw his reflection in the glass of the main door. What if Charles were right? Wouldn't it be wonderful if Balard did actually desire his assistance in some sort of an experiment? It would be such a great honor. But there was scant chance of that, he told himself, staring at his reflection. He was twenty-three years old and short of stature and a bit stooped in the shoulders. His features were much too blunt and one could hardly see his eyes behind the thick spectacles. And he looked thoroughly uncomfortable in his best suit, a thing of heavy black cloth. There was nothing about him, he decided, that would inspire Balard to single him out from all the other young chemists in Paris for a special assignment. Well . . . better to expect nothing than to be disappointed. He sighed and pushed the door open.

Inside, the building was cool and drafty. There was the odor of floor polish and chalk dust in the air. From rooms on both sides of the high-ceilinged corridor came the murmur of student voices.

"Good morning, Monsieur Pasteur."

The owner of the voice—a man in his late forties—stood

just inside the front door. He was of medium height and barrel-chested. His forehead was high, his features rather heavy, and his hair, cut in the style of the day, curled down over his ears. He wore a dark suit. The points of a high collar stabbed the underside of his chin.

"Good morning, Professor Dumas," Louis said, surprised to see his favorite teacher.

Jean Baptiste Dumas, who—like Balard—had achieved international fame as a chemist, took from his vest pocket a gold watch the size of a potato and glanced at it. "You're punctual, as usual. Let's not keep Balard waiting."

Louis blinked in astonishment. "You're coming in with me?"

"Of course. I was with Balard when he wrote the note last night. Now I want to be on hand to see your expression when he tells you his news."

"Professor! What's this all about?"

Already Dumas was striding along the corridor. "You'll know very soon."

Louis fell in alongside the man, who, more than any other person he knew, had influenced the course of his life. Three years ago, Louis had come from his village of Arbois in southeastern France to study for the teaching profession at the École Normale. But, interested in science since childhood, he had also attended the classes of Dumas at the Sorbonne. The professor, with his fiery lectures and demonstrations, had opened to him the wonders of chemistry. From his earliest days with Dumas, Louis had known that he too belonged in the chemical laboratory—there could be no other career for him.

Their route carried them past busy classrooms to Balard's

laboratory door. The lab was actually a suite of four small rooms, all of them cluttered with work tables, retorts, flasks, and row upon row of test tubes. Scribbling in a notebook in the first of these rooms was the man who, at the age of twenty-four, had discovered the chemical element bromine.

Antoine Balard was now middle-aged, but he bounded up from his work table like a young boy and greeted his visitors effusively. Louis grinned. As usual, everything about Balard was in disarray. His smock was open and flapped about his legs, its huge pockets bulging with scraps of note-paper. His gray hair seemed to be standing on end, and somehow he had smudged the tip of his large, blunt nose.

"Come. We'll talk in my office."

The "office" proved to be but a corner of the adjoining room furnished with a cluttered desk, two chairs painted a hideous red, and a cot. Louis sat on the edge of the cot with Dumas standing at his side, and Balard dropped into a chair by the desk. A broad smile wrinkled his moon face.

"My note mystified you, eh?"

"That's putting it mildly, sir."

Balard laughed a barking laugh. "I thought so. You must forgive me. It is a bad habit—but I do enjoy tickling someone's curiosity."

Now the chemist leaned forward, his manner abruptly serious. "Professor Dumas and I have watched you closely in our classes for a long time. We feel you show great promise."

"Thank you." Louis inclined his head. The compliment should have thrilled him. But he was too concerned with waiting to know what Balard wanted of him really to hear it.

"Yes, great promise. Let me see . . ." Balard pawed at the

papers on his desk, and finally found the one he wanted. "Here it is. A fine record. Out of fourteen candidates in the recent examination for a professorship, you were the third of the four who passed. Your work in chemistry and physics caused the jury to write, 'He will make an excellent professor.'"

Louis nodded. A little impatiently. Would Balard never come to the point?

Balard tossed the paper aside. "Tell me, how have you earned money during your Paris school years?"

"By tutoring pupils at Monsieur Barbet's School."

"But now that you are a licensed teacher at work on your Doctor of Science degree, you would like to devote all your time to chemistry?"

"Oh, yes, sir."

"And Professor Dumas and I think you should. So a little idea has come to mind. How would you like a position as an assistant in my laboratory?"

Louis stared. Balard had spoken so casually that Louis was not certain he had heard correctly. "What did you say, sir? A position?"

"Yes."

"A—" Louis swallowed on the next word and felt a thorough fool—"*full-time* position?"

"Yes." Balard was smiling now and massaging the tip of his nose with short, fleshy fingers and peering at Louis from beneath cocked eyebrows. "The idea appeals to you?"

Louis gaped from Balard to Dumas and back again. Slowly, he digested the significance of Balard's proposal. Months of study and preparation for work in the field he loved had come, with one deliberately casual remark, to an

end; in a single moment, all the hours of dreaming had
become reality. He tried to voice his feelings. But he only
heard himself blurting out inanely, "Oh, yes! Yes. It's just
the sort of thing I've always wanted. I can't thank you
enough. . . ."

He stumbled over his words, but Balard waved carelessly,
as if stumbling and inanity were the exact things he had
expected at this moment. "No thanks are necessary," he
said. "You deserve whatever help we can give you. Now
about your duties. At first, you'll do some filing work for me.
Also I have some experiments I want you to observe. Naturally, you'll have adequate time for your own researches
and studies. I'll expect you to start tomorrow morning—at
eight sharp."

"I won't be late. You can count on that. And thank you
again—"

"No more of that," Balard intervened, adding with a
severity that he couldn't quite bring off, "I want only one
thing from you—hard work."

In a few minutes, the interview came to an end, and a
completely dazed Louis found himself again in the street.

"What's the matter?" Charles Chappuis demanded when
he saw his friend's expression. Then, not waiting for an
answer, he shouted, "No! Don't tell me—I can guess. He
wants you to help him with an experiment. I was right!"

"Much better than that," Louis said. He was grinning
crazily. He was dimly conscious of the stares of passers-by
as he pounded Charles on the shoulder and related the story
of the interview.

Even before the young chemist had finished, Charles
said, "Congratulations! I told you something fine would

happen. Now come along." He grasped Louis' arm and began to hurry along the glistening sidewalk. They made an odd looking pair, one thin and striding, the other chunky and stumbling, both with faces flushed and hands gesticulating excitedly. "We must celebrate. We're going to find a restaurant and I'm going to fill you up with the best food on the menu. I had to do this when you were a student and always forgot to eat. Now that you're a full-fledged laboratory assistant, you'll be doing the same thing again."

Louis pulled his friend to a halt. "Wait. Just a moment. There is something I must do first."

"Yes?"

"I must write my family about what has happened. Then we can think of celebrating."

"Of course." Charles nodded understandingly. "I should have known you'd want to write to them immediately." It was an old Pasteur custom with which he had been long acquainted, this writing to the family of every exciting—and, more often, unexciting—detail of daily existence. Louis' parents were simple people, out of the main stream of life, and their son was their great hope and great adventure.

Quickly, the young men returned to Louis' room at Monsieur Barbet's School on the left bank of the Seine. Words flowed from Louis' pen; and memories of the people to whom he was writing—his father, mother, and three sisters —flooded his mind. His father, Joseph, was a tanner, a broad-shouldered man of simple tastes who had once been a soldier in Napoleon's army and who now spent his spare time painting pictures. His mother's name was Jeanne; she was the daughter of a farmer. They had been living at Dole at the time of Louis' birth on December 27, 1822, but had moved to Arbois when their son was four.

Louis, his quill pen scratching noisily across the page, remembered what a happy life these two had given him at Arbois. There had been work to do in the tannery and toys to play with that his father had fashioned. There had been glorious days of swimming in the Cuisance River. And there had been school. Louis had first attended the primary school at Arbois; then, because his father wanted him to have the best education possible, at fourteen he had been sent to Monsieur Barbet's School to prepare for the École Normale.

That first Paris venture had been a disappointment for both father and son. Louis had grown so homesick that Joseph had had to come to Barbet's to fetch him back to Arbois. But things had turned out well. Louis had attended the Royal College of Besançon near Arbois and, after earning his Bachelor of Arts Degree, he had resolved to return to Paris and enter the École Normale.

And now here he was, a graduate of that fine school and employed by one of the foremost scientists in France. The last words of the letter were written. He sat back with an affectionate sigh. He owed his parents so much. They had given him an education and that education had brought him to the threshold of a life's work.

A life's work in the laboratory. It was a prospect that left him a little breathless.

The Riddle of
the Crystals

"Louis," Balard called. "May I speak with you a moment here in my office?"

"Right away, Professor."

Louis raised his face from a microscope, scribbled a last sentence in his notebook, and crossed the gloomy laboratory to the even gloomier adjoining room. He felt the dull ache of stiffness low in his back. He smiled. It was a good pain, a memento of long hours spent over a work bench in deep concentration.

Balard was seated at his desk, his pumpkin-shaped head with its flurry of gray hair silhouetted against a window revealing a leaden December sky. A chill wind, sounding like a lost ghost, moaned along the side of the building and, for a brief moment, Louis was shocked to realize how swiftly time had passed. When first he had come to work for Balard, the trees outside were deep in gold-green foliage and bright summer frocks were still to be seen on Paris streets. But, some time during the countless hours of research and experimentation, winter had stolen upon the city. The trees were naked and the people wore heavy dark topcoats and walked with their shoulders hunched against the slanting rain.

Balard jumped to his feet, his spirits not at all dulled by such a miserable day. His tie was loose and crooked, his pockets bulging, and his smile broad. "Ah, Louis, there's someone here I want you to meet."

A tall, lean man, whom Louis had seen enter the lab earlier, rose from the all-but-collapsing chair alongside the desk and extended his hand. "This is Monsieur Auguste Laurent," the professor explained. "He has left his teaching duties at Bordeaux to work with us."

Louis accepted Auguste Laurent's hand. He was pleased with what he felt and saw. The man's fingers were like steel wires and there was fire in the eyes set deep in the thin face. Louis had been around people like Balard and Dumas long enough to recognize a truly dedicated scientist when he saw one. He knew immediately that the lab had gained a fine worker.

"I've heard of you, sir," he said. "You are greatly respected as a chemist here in Paris."

Laurent's smile was slight and reserved, but it lit up his eyes. "Thank you."

"And you shall hear much more of him, Louis," Balard said. "In fact, you'll hear of him every day. But you tell him, Auguste."

"My work here in the laboratory will be to test the accuracy of certain present-day chemical theories," Laurent said. "Professor Balard has told me of your studies and—"

Balard was not one to let another talk too long if he himself knew what was to be said and now he could not resist the urge to break in excitedly, "And so Monsieur Laurent would be most pleased if you would consent to help him with these experiments!"

Even before Balard finished speaking, Louis realized what he had in mind. Delight flooded him and his answer came swiftly. "Of course I'll help Monsieur Laurent. It will be an honor."

He felt Balard's elbow nudge his ribs, saw the professor's almost childlike smile. "I always seem to be full of surprises for you, don't I?"

Louis nodded. "Yes. Perhaps someday I'll get used to them."

Already his mind was running to the days ahead. What did this new task mean to him? So many things—forgotten meals, the increasingly familiar ache low in his back, burning eyes glued to a microscope in the silent hours long after the lights of Paris had gone out. But who cared? Who could pass up such an opportunity to do more work and study in the field he loved so deeply. What a fine, long letter would be written home tonight!

But what Louis Pasteur could not know, standing there in the gloom of the late afternoon and questioning Laurent about the coming experiments, was that this quiet, proud newcomer from Bordeaux would set him on the path to his first great scientific adventure.

The first step along that path was taken one morning some weeks later when Laurent glanced up from his microscope and called:

"Louis."

No response came from the young man across the work bench. His head was bent far over the notebook in which he was writing.

Laurent suppressed an amused sigh and then called quite loudly:

"Louis!"

The head snapped up and in the eyes behind the thick glasses was a look of surprise. It was an expression anyone who worked with Pasteur and interrupted his concentration knew only too well.

"I'm sorry, Monsieur Laurent. Had you called often?"

Laurent shook his head. "I should hate to have to rouse you if the building were on fire." He beckoned Louis to his side of the table. "If I remember correctly, Professor Balard said you are interested in crystals."

"Oh, yes." The very mention of these minute chunks of solid matter that emerged from chemical solutions caused Louis to hasten to Laurent's side. "They have fascinated me since I first studied them in Professor Delafosse's class at the École Normale. In fact, I'm writing the thesis for my Doctor's degree on them."

"Then I think this will interest you." Laurent indicated his microscope and Louis put his eye to it. "I've been studying tungstate of soda. It's produced some very interesting crystalline formations."

Louis sighed in agreement. The tungstate was perfectly crystallized and very pure. The circle of yellow-white light below the eyepiece of the microscope was filled with mountains of oddly shaped, tiny chips of ice.

"Do you notice anything strange about the crystals?" Laurent asked, and then went on without waiting for an answer. "Look closely and you'll see that the tungstate has produced three distinct types of crystals."

Yes. He was right. If you looked closely, if you peered along every ridge and into every valley of the glistening mountain range, you could see the differences in shape, the subtle differences of angles and facets that distinguished each type. Louis straightened as Laurent said, "Imagine. That is a portion of tungstate so small I could place it in my hand and blow it away with a single breath. Yet it can produce several types of crystals. I'm forever amazed at these examples of nature's work."

"So am I. One of the things that amazes me most is the crystals' effect on polarized light. If a beam of light is passed through certain crystals, such as tartaric acid or sugar in solution, that beam will be bent to the right. Other crystals —those of quinine and the essences of turpentine, for instance—will bend it to the left. In this way, the crystals themselves give the scientist a clue to the elements within them."

Neither man could know at that moment the important part this light-bending trait of the crystals would someday play in industry and medicine. In future years, the saccharimeter, built on the principle of polarized light, would be used by physicians treating diabetes, and by manufacturers computing the amount of pure sugar in commercial brown sugar.

Louis moved to a nearby work stool. He sat down, his face thoughtful, his chin supported in the palm of one hand. "Those crystals reminded me of something that interested me greatly when I was at the École Normale," he said at length.

"And what is that?"

"Mitscherlich's riddle."

Laurent smiled. "I know it well. It's thoroughly confused the finest minds in chemistry for years."

"Let me see if I recall it. I once knew it by heart," Louis said. "I believe it was in 1844 that Eilhardt Mitscherlich first published his riddle in Germany. He wrote that he had tested with light the crystals of tartaric acid and those of paratartaric acid (or, as it is sometimes called, racemic acid). When he passed a light beam through the tartrate crystals, it was bent to the right."

"Correct."

"But," Louis continued, his voice rising with the same excitement he had felt when first reading Mitscherlich's report, "when he passed a light beam through the paratartrate crystals, he found they reflected *no light at all!*"

Laurent picked up the story. "Which was very strange, because both solutions are exactly alike in every way. Both have crystals of the same shape, and the nature and number of the atoms and their arrangement are identical."

"Then why should the tartaric acid bend the plane of polarized light and the paratartaric acid reflect no light at all? It doesn't make sense!"

"Of course not." The usually somber Laurent broke into a laugh. "That's the big riddle. As I say, it's confused every chemist in Europe. Answer it and you'll be famous. There's no telling how important the answer might be to science— what it might show us about the mysterious behavior of microscopic things, what discoveries and improvements in chemistry and medicine and industry it might lead to."

Mitscherlich's riddle haunted Louis the rest of the morning. By noontime, he had made up his mind to investigate the tartrate and paratartrate crystals that had so confounded the German chemist. He told himself he was not deliberately setting out to solve the mystery; older and more experienced minds than his had failed at that task. Rather, he looked upon the study as a device for developing his skill in the use of light-testing equipment. Too, the crystals were beautiful things to behold and he had to admit he wanted to work with them for the sheer joy of it.

The smile of anticipation that lighted his face dissolved abruptly when he looked up to see Balard at his side. The professor's expression startled him. Balard's complexion was a deep red. Anger poured out of his usually friendly eyes.

"Planning some new experiment, Louis?"

"As a matter of fact, yes," Louis said, puzzled by the brittleness of Balard's tone. Had he done something to offend his employer?

"Well, I hope you have a chance to get to it." Balard's hand shot forward and in it was a sheet of parchment paper, crumpled by his angry grasp. "This came in the mail for you today. I opened it by mistake."

Louis smoothed the paper with hands that Balard's strange attitude had set to trembling. At the top was the crest of the Ministry of Education. Louis read the short message, written in a thin, erect script and set down in the exact center of the page. Blood drained from his face. He read the message again. And then again. His whole world seemed to crash about his feet.

"It's from the Minister of Education," he managed to say stupidly. "He wants to send me away."

Laurent glanced up from his work across the table. "What's that?"

Until then, Balard had managed to keep quiet. Now he exploded. His arms shot outward in a gesture of helpless exasperation. His hair seemed to stand right on end. "Our grand minister! He who is supposed to be so wise! He who has the fate of thousands of young teachers in his hands! He is a fool! A complete fool! An idiot!" His fist descended to the work table and set rows of test tubes rattling. His voice echoed round the room like high-pitched thunder. "He wants to send young Pasteur to teach at the Tournon Lycée at Ardeche! Think of it! He wants to take him from the lab and send him five hundred kilometers from Paris, the very heart of the French scientific world!"

Laurent shrugged. "But he has the power to do that. It is the custom."

"Custom, bah!" Balard snorted. "It is a custom I shall be most happy to break into a thousand—no! a million— pieces." His bulky figure swung towards the door. "Come along, Louis. We're going to have this out with our Monsieur Minister!"

Louis came hesitantly to his feet. "Now?"

Balard flung the front door open. "Yes! Now! Right now! Immediately!" He held the door wide for the advancing Louis. "I'll teach him not to waste good talent . . ."

"Professor Balard. Louis," Auguste Laurent called with exaggerated mildness.

"Yes?"

"Don't you think you'd make a better impression on the minister if you exchanged your smocks for coats?"

Had Louis been in better spirits, he would have laughed.

And he would have smiled, too, at the frightened manner in which a clerk at the Ministry scurried into the minister's office to inform him that someone who seemed to be a madman was demanding to see him. The minister himself, rotund and bearded, greeted Balard warily.

"What can I do for you, Professor?"

Balard dropped like a potato sack into a chair. He waved the letter at the minister. "You're going to send my assistant, Pasteur, to Ardeche?" He smiled sweetly.

"That is correct."

"It is sheer folly! Stupid!" Balard roared with a sudden violence that rocked the minister back in his chair. Louis felt his heart sink. He had hoped Balard might do some good. But none would be done this way. "This boy shows great promise as a scientist. You are going to destroy him by exiling him to some tiny spot. He will accomplish nothing. His mind and his talent will rot!"

The minister held up pleading hands. "A moment, Professor, a moment, please! Anger will get us nowhere. Please calm yourself. You cannot expect me to change my decision."

Louis watched Balard make a visible effort to control himself. When the chemist spoke again, his voice was a rumbling thing, a volcano trying hard not to erupt. "But I *do* expect you to change it. I demand that you do so. This boy is a dedicated laboratory worker. He asks nothing more than to be allowed to remain at his bench day and night. Do you know what his friends call him—a 'laboratory pillar.' But they call him that with great respect, because they sense, as do I, that one day he may bring great honor to French science." He shook a finger at the minister. "Mark my words, you will deprive him of that chance if you send him away. Let him remain in Paris. Let him learn and work. There will be time to send him away later."

"But," the minister shrugged, "a man is needed at Ardeche immediately—"

The volcano was starting to erupt. "Then send someone else! Leave this boy to his work. He belongs in the laboratory. Here! I will prove it. When he was a student, one of his professors lectured on how to produce phosphorus. Was a lecture enough to satisfy Pasteur? It was not! He was not content until he had purchased some bones, burned them, treated their ashes with sulfuric acid and manufactured phosphorus on his own. Not one other student did this. Only Pasteur. I tell you, he is marked for greatness. And let me tell you something else—"

The minister waved Balard to silence. "Enough, Professor, enough. I believe you. Now give me a moment to think."

Louis watched the minister breathlessly, not daring to hope that Balard had accomplished the impossible, not daring to hope that the minister might change his mind and allow him to remain at the lab. When the official spoke again, Louis almost shouted aloud with relief and happiness.

"All right, Professor. I will find someone to take his place at Ardeche. He will have his chance to continue his work a little longer. But—" the minister tapped his desk for emphasis—"he will be called again someday soon. At that time I will put up with no arguments. Is that clear?"

Balard, the battle over, nodded tiredly. The minister, too, looked worn as he accepted Louis' hand and heard the young man's words of gratitude. He smiled wanly. "The professor is a very eloquent man. You are fortunate to have him on your side."

Outside, Louis attempted to thank Balard for that eloquence. The chemist waved airily. "It wasn't difficult at all. The minister is really a very sensible fellow." He paused and winked. "At times. And now let's get back to work. I want to hear all about this new experiment you have in mind."

The First Discovery

The stormy interview with the minister had exhausted and unnerved Louis, but, upon his return to the lab, he immediately began preparing for his study of crystals. He felt he had no time to waste. At any moment, the minister could decide his teaching services were again needed elsewhere and bring to an abrupt conclusion this all-important phase of his life.

Some days later he was able to tell Laurent the plan of study he had formulated. "I intend to begin with tartaric acid and all its combinations. Then I shall turn to paratartaric acid."

"What do you think you'll find?"

"I don't know. But I have certain hopes."

"And they are?"

"Well, Mitscherlich and other scientists claim that the tartaric acid and the paratartaric acid crystals are identical in every way. I don't see how that can be. If they were, both types would bend light in the same way. There must be some difference, some very tiny difference in their shapes."

"And you hope to find that difference?"

Louis nodded. "I'm certainly going to try."

"I wish you luck," Laurent said. "It will be a mighty task—finding something that experts such as Mitscherlich could not locate. I'll be interested in seeing how things turn out."

Laurent, however, was not destined to witness the end of the study. A short time later he accepted a position as assistant to Professor Dumas and moved to the Sorbonne where he earned a reputation for controversial and thought-provoking lectures. And so he passed out of Louis' life. But the young chemist would always fondly remember him as the man who started him on his first great scientific adventure.

Louis' work for his Doctor of Science degree interrupted the crystal study for long periods during the next year, 1847. He gave much time to the completion of his theses. For chemistry, his paper was entitled, "Researches into the Saturation Capacity of Arsenious Acid: A Study of the Arsenites of Potash, Soda, and Ammonia," while his physics essay bore the title, "Study of Phenomena Relative to the Rotary Polarization of Liquids." They were dedicated to his mother and father, and were presented, somewhat nervously, to his examining professors on August 23, 1847.

There was no reason for his nervousness. His parents soon learned that their son had traveled far beyond their greatest expectations. He had won his Doctor's degree.

Then, in the early days of 1848, a revolution broke out in France which resulted in the abdication of King Louis Philippe. The young chemist was inspired by visions of a free republic. He gave all his savings—one hundred and fifty francs—to the cause, and enlisted in the National Guard, a city militia for keeping the peace. He passed the days of unrest on guard duty in the cold, drafty Orleans Railway Station.

Only when peace was restored did he get down to real work on his study. Slowly, painstakingly, he investigated the crystals of nineteen combinations of tartaric acid. It was back-breaking labor. He compared each of his observations with those of the noted crystallographer, de la Provostaye. And he was forced to build for himself the needed goniometer and polarimeter, instruments for measuring angles and degrees of polarization in light.

"Good! Good!" Balard cried when informed of this latter fact. "Hardship! It's the best thing in the world for you! It will teach you self-discipline—something needed by every scientist who is ever going to be worth his salt!"

Balard was further delighted to learn how many hours were required to check each lot of crystals.

"Young Pasteur spends so much time at his microscope," he told a friend, "that he must see his beloved crystals hovering in the air before his eyes as he walks along the street or tries to eat and sleep!"

But very soon Louis knew that he had found something that amply compensated for his burning eyes and cotton-filled head. The joy of discovery was upon him, for the little tartrate crystals had revealed one of their most well-kept secrets to him. In the side of each, hidden away among other surface angles and grooves, was a tiny facet—or face. These facets were so small that, apparently, even the great Mitscherlich and de la Provostaye had missed them.

Louis cradled his forehead in the palm of his hand and

murmured thoughtfully, "These little facets must cause tartaric acid to bend a light beam to the right. Let me see. They must catch the light and, just like a mirror, reflect it in that direction. Yes. Yes. That must be it!" Because of the position of their facets, he called the tiny chunks of matter "right-handed crystals."

He couldn't be blamed for a moment of quiet gloating. "Well, well! What do you think of that! You've seen something that no one else has seen!"

Suddenly a startling thought drove him to tense silence. The impact of it left him feeling light-headed, slightly dizzy. The thought whispered that he, so young and inexperienced, just might have stumbled on the answer to Mitscherlich's riddle. But no! It couldn't be! The answer was too simple to accomplish anything so wonderful. It was so simple it was almost laughable.

He spoke slowly to himself. "If right-handed crystals bend light to the right, then perhaps the reason why the paratartrate crystals are incapable of bending light is that they have no facets at all!"

He sat back, hardly daring to breathe. If that were so, the solution of the mystery would be his. He closed his eyes tight. It was very possible he was approaching the gates of fame. If only they would swing open before him!

Quickly, he prepared solutions of paratartaric acid and its salts and examined their crystals. His heart pounded wildly. Elation wiped lines of fatigue from his face. So far so good. Each batch of crystals showed him not one little facet characteristic of the tartrates.

But what was this? He was now examining the paratartrate of sodium-ammonium, a substance which Mitscherlich had mentioned in particular. Disappointment flooded him. The little facets were here! Exactly as in the tartrates. His elation evaporated. The mystery was not solved, after all. The gates of fame were still locked to him.

But perhaps not! Something about the maddening crystals pushed itself into his vision as he stared at them time and time again—something odd in their glistening, irregular structures. His fist thumped the work bench when he realized what that odd something was. Many of the crystals had facets in their right sides. But there were others with the facets glowing and winking in their left walls. They were left-handed crystals.

"So that's it! You're really a combination of *two* types of crystals. What a secret you've kept all these years. You've kept it from Mitscherlich and de la Provostaye and all the others who have peered at you. But I've found you out!"

A new idea, more exciting than its predecessor, surged through him. Perhaps the mystery could yet be solved. The next minutes—no, the next hours—would tell.

Like a bloodhound in pursuit of a criminal, he began to separate the two types of crystals. He placed the right-handed ones near one elbow, the left-handed ones near the other. Before the job was done, his wrists and fingers ached and sweat fogged his glasses. Lunchtime came and went, but he was totally unaware of any hunger pangs. The world could have come to an end and he would probably not have known it.

At last the crystals were separated. Three steps remained before his idea could be proved. He started on the first step without a moment's rest, without even stretching his arms to relieve their stiffness.

He poured the right-handed crystals into a solution and placed them in the polarimeter. He watched light from a burner pass through the solution bottle, strike a prism directly behind the bottle, and flicker to the upper right side of a small screen at the end of the apparatus. Louis clenched his fists in satisfaction. The crystals bent light in exactly the same manner as the tartrates.

Now the left-handed crystals went into solution and into the polarimeter. The light pierced the bottle and prism and appeared, dancing, on the left side of the screen. Step two was complete.

Louis' mouth was dry. He badly wanted a drink of water, but was powerless to tear himself from his work. Step three remained. It was the giant step, the one that would prove or shatter his idea. If it proved the idea, fame would be his; the mystery would be solved.

He mixed equal weights of the two types of crystals in solution. He walked on unsteady legs to the polarimeter. Into the apparatus he pushed the solution bottle, releasing it quickly, as if it were a scalding thing. He dragged his gaze to the small screen . . .

Happiness. Relief. Triumph. All these things flooded his whole being. Not one single flash of light was visible on the screen! He looked again and then again to make certain. He turned the bottle slightly. No light. Absolutely no light.

His face, so hard and tense a moment ago, became the face of a delighted child. He strode through the lab in search of Balard, in search of anyone to whom he could shout the news that Mitscherlich's riddle was a riddle no longer. The lab was deserted. He threw open the front door and charged directly into a young assistant passing along the hall.

The young assistant must have thought him demented. Louis flung his arms about the fellow's shoulders. Broken sentences erupted from his lips.

"I have just made a great discovery—I am so happy that, look, I am shaking all over and am unable to set my eyes again to the polarimeter!" He pulled the assistant along the hall to the front entrance and through cold sunshine to the Luxembourg Gardens. He talked all the while. His glasses were tilted crazily on his nose. His eyes were glistening blue marbles. Only when he had dropped to a park bench did the story of his adventure become coherent.

"In the tartrates, the right-handed crystals are present; in some of the paratartrates, there are no facets. But, in the paratartrate of sodium-ammonium, there are both right- and left-handed crystals. Each is capable of bending light in a certain direction. But when they are mixed together, each group *neutralizes* the other, causing no light at all to be seen!"

He slapped his knees with open palms. "Do you realize what this means? It means I've solved Mitscherlich's riddle and have unearthed two brand new types of crystals! I feel like an explorer who has stumbled upon a new land."

Balard's excitement equaled Louis' when he learned of his young helper's achievement. With his customary exuberance, he broadcast the news to all areas of the Paris scientific world and sought out at the Academy of Sciences the most respected of all French chemists, Jean-Baptiste Biot.

Biot was seventy-four. He had heard many amazing things in his long life, amazing things that often turned out to be ridiculous mistakes. And so he heard Balard's words with skepticism and said, "I've worked on this Mitscherlich thing myself. So have the best minds in Europe. Do you mean to tell me a boy of twenty-six has achieved success where we failed?"

"I do."

Biot grinned at the certainty in Balard's tone. The tip of his hawklike nose dipped almost to his upper lip. "You will forgive me if I do not believe this until I see it for myself. Send your young genius to me. I shall find out soon enough if he's made some sort of error."

Before Louis could meet Biot, tragic news came from Arbois. His mother had died a few hours after an attack of apoplexy. His work and the joy of his discovery were forgotten in his grief. He journeyed home to attend her funeral. The sorrow of her passing was with him for weeks. In her quiet way, she had filled his early years with love and, in later times, had greatly encouraged him in his work. In a future year, when a memorial plate was affixed to his birthplace at Dole, he would say of her, "Your enthusiasm, my dear mother, you have passed on to me. If I have associated greatness of science with greatness of country, it was because you instilled these sentiments in me, you inspired me."

At last he had to think of his work again and returned to Paris. He arranged the first of several appointments with Biot at the old man's rooms at the Collège de France. His first sight of this scientist-adventurer, whose interests ranged from chemistry to astronomy, and who had made the world's first balloon ascent for scientific purposes, unnerved him. The old fellow's body was lean, his face long, and his every feature prominent. His forehead was high and crisscrossed with deep grooves. He carried himself regally, but his head was thrust forward slightly, defiantly, as if he were constantly and ruthlessly in search of truth and falsity in science and man alike.

He greeted Louis with a smile of doubt and the words, "So you've answered Mitscherlich and found some new crystals, have you? Well, we shall see. Come over here, young man, and mix the paratartrate of sodium-ammonium for me."

Louis was uncomfortably aware of shrewd eyes boring into him as he performed this task. Sunlight, flowing through a window, may have softened the stark whiteness of Biot's hair, but it hardened his lined face into a suspicious mask. He was waiting, poised like an ancient eagle, ready to swoop down on any error in the preparation that would prove the crystal discovery a failure. And if some error should make itself known—well, the old man's sharp tongue and impatience with anything less than perfection were legends in Paris. Louis knew he would suffer a tongue-lashing that would sting for a lifetime.

When the solution was prepared, Biot himself carried it to a cupboard. He wagged a slender, large-knuckled finger. "It will remain here until the crystals are formed. Until then, no one must touch it. Come back tomorrow at the same time."

The next day, Biot, snorting now and again, peered over Louis' shoulder as the young man separated the right- and left-handed crystals. He dipped a long nose to the tiny heap of left-handed ones.

"Humph! Left-handed ones, you say?"

"Yes, sir."

"They look no different from the others. Well, we shall

see." How many times the ancient eagle had made that statement during his two meetings with Louis! Biot now said, "Go into the other room. I'll put the crystals in solution myself. And don't go walking about and making a lot of noise. And don't come knocking at the door. I'll call you when I want you. This is too important to be upset by any petty distractions."

The minutes spent in the adjoining room dragged horribly for Louis. He knew he faced his final test. What if something should go wrong? Suppose he *had* made some sort of mistake through inexperience and impetuosity. Suppose he had discovered nothing at all! Suppose, suppose, suppose! Nonsense! Stop it! Everything went right in the lab. Everything will go right now. This old man is just scaring you to death . . .

"All right," Biot said from the doorway, "I'm ready."

Louis moved woodenly into the room. Biot stepped to a Soleil polarimeter. He gripped a solution bottle.

"We'll first test what you say are the left-handed crystals. If they bend light to the left, I'll know your discovery is really valid. And I'll know I'm looking at a scientist who has found greatness. But if they don't . . ."

Biot left the sentence unfinished. The warning in his eyes spoke more eloquently than words. He turned to the polarimeter and placed the bottle in it. He stooped low, his white head thrust forward stiffly as he followed the light beam. Louis held his breath. Then he saw a flicker of light on the screen in the apparatus. It fluttered to the left!

Biot straightened slowly. He turned to Louis, studying the young man closely, as if really seeing him for the first time. No longer were the long planes of his face hard with doubt.

A soft warmth glowed in his every feature. A smile lifted the corners of his thin lips and Louis wondered why he had ever been frightened of this great scientist. Biot gripped his hand. He needed no more proof. Louis' discovery of hitherto unknown crystals was validated. It was only a routine matter to check the right-handed crystals and then see that both groups neutralized each other in solution.

Louis thought he saw tears behind the old man's eyes. The bony fingers that held his hand trembled. "My dear son, I have loved science so much that this stirs my heart."

These words were to ring in Louis' ears for the rest of his life. They would humble him in moments of triumph and support him in times of failure, in times when the world of science appeared set against him. But now they meant but one thing. He had proved his findings to one of France's greatest scientists. The gates of fame were opening to him and beyond those gates lay more work—endless hours of work in searching out the unknown.

Strassburg and
Marie Laurent

On January 15, 1849, Louis sat by the window of a train that was moving cautiously over snow-wet tracks in southeastern France. He wore a heavy but rather threadbare topcoat. Draped over his ears and tucked beneath his hat was a woolen scarf. Through breaking clouds of engine smoke, he glimpsed the passing landscape. The rolling, gray-white countryside was a patchwork of forest stands, straw-roofed farmhouses, and tiny villages clustered about gaunt, flaking church spires.

Eight months had passed since the afternoon Biot had gripped his hand at the Collège de France, eight whirlwind months crowded with both happy and unhappy events. On the bright side, his discovery had earned him the praise of distinguished scientists three times his age. He had been told countless times that he had made an invaluable contribution to that branch of chemistry which investigates molecular structures in nature—stereochemistry. Biot had suggested they work together and, guided by the old man, Louis had published a paper concerning his crystal study, "Researches on the Relations Which May Exist between Crystalline Form, Chemical Composition, and the Direction of Rotary Power." As they had worked together, Louis had come to realize that the chemist's respect for him was developing into an affection like that of father for son.

But, on the unhappy side, in November he had been ordered by the Minister of Education to a teaching post at the Lycée at Dijon. No amount of protesting by Biot, Dumas, and Balard had altered the decision. All in all, his stay at Dijon had been unpleasant. He'd missed the Paris lab and the Lycée had afforded him only meager quarters for his experiments. Not that there had been time for experiments. He'd spent countless hours trying to prepare interesting lectures and demonstrations for classes that often had as many as eighty boys in them.

Now, as the train entered the station at Strassburg, he sighed with relief. Surely the bad times were over. Quite suddenly, through the help of friends, he had been appointed Assistant Professor of Chemistry at the University of Strassburg, a fine school in a very beautiful city.

No sooner had he descended to the platform with his two valises than he heard his name called by a familiar voice. He turned to see the portly figure of Pierre Bertin, a one-time fellow student at the École Normale and now Professor of Physics at Strassburg, come trundling through the crowd. Bertin tipped his hat in comic fashion (everything this easy-going person did amused Louis) to a lady he had accidentally jostled. Then, smiling broadly, he grasped Louis' hand.

"Welcome, my friend, welcome! You look terrible. Overworked and underfed! But I shall take care of that." Now he had the valises in hand and was leading Louis out of the station, talking happily and swiftly over the heads of other disembarking passengers. "I understand you've become quite the famous scientist. Great discoveries and all that sort of thing. You'll have to buy a new topcoat. That one doesn't suit your new-found dignity at all. This valise weighs a ton. What have you got in it—a complete lab?"

Louis managed to halt the flow of words at the station entrance. "Pierre, do you mind if I manage to thank you for insisting I live at your home while at the university?"

Bertin's oval face puckered, his eyes almost disappearing behind heavy pouches. He prodded Louis' middle with a pudgy forefinger. His hat was tilted at a rakish angle. "Bah! No more of that. I intend to bask in the glory of my very clever scientific friend from Paris. I will tell everyone that I always knew you were destined for glory. Then they will think that I, too, am a genius—which I am not. Now let's get home and see your rooms."

The suite of rooms delighted Louis. They were airy and comfortable. After he had unpacked and bathed, he was taken on a tour of the university by his host. The trip brought them eventually to the school laboratories.

"They're not very good, I'm afraid," Pierre apologized. "Dusty. Much too small. Poorly lighted and inadequately equipped."

Louis nodded briskly, annoyed. He picked up a microscope, turned it slowly in his hands. It was a crude affair, cheaply made, its base cracked. He felt his temper flare. "It's like this all over France! The greatest of our scientists— even men like Balard, Dumas, and Biot—are made to work with the poorest of equipment. And they have to beg and sometimes lie to obtain adequate space.

"Take Balard. When the École Normale moved to new quarters several years ago, he had to fool the heads of the school into giving him a lab. He told them he needed rooms for the display of scientific collections. If he hadn't done that, he probably would have had to conduct his experiments out on the pavement.

"But it won't be like this always! It can't be. Someday France must awaken to the fact that its greatest glory is to be found in its scientists."

Pierre held up his hands, palms forward, fingers widespread. "Please, Louis! Save your lectures for the Minister of Education and your classes. I agree with you wholeheartedly. But I must say I'm very surprised. When you were at the École Normale you were the shy, quiet bookworm of the school." He shook his head in mock sadness. "But now look at you. You've become a real tiger."

"Well, it makes me angry," Louis said. "How can France hope to have its men of the laboratory continue battling to improve industry and ease the sufferings of mankind in such makeshift surroundings? And yet they manage to do just that—and magnificently!"

"Bravo, Monsieur."

The words were spoken from the doorway by an elderly man of medium height. Pierre introduced this newcomer, who wore his dignity as easily as his well-tailored clothes, as Auguste Laurent, the Rector of Strassburg Academy.

"Are you, by any chance, related to Auguste Laurent, the chemist?" Louis asked. "He was once of great help to me."

"No. We both bear the same name and I have heard of him, but he is not a relation." The Rector touched a silver-gray temple and glanced about the laboratory. "Though our facilities are not the best, Monsieur Pasteur, I hope you will be happy here at the university. My house is a gathering place for the members of the faculty. I'd like you to know that it is always open to you. Perhaps you and Pierre would consent to take dinner with my family this evening?"

Pierre, long acquainted with the fine table the Rector set, was quick to reply, "I think that's a splendid idea."

It also proved to be an idea that affected the entire course of Louis' life, for that night marked his first meeting with Marie Laurent. After he had bowed, stiffly and shyly, to the Rector's wife and older daughter, he was introduced to this dark-haired girl of twenty-two and saw her smile and heard her say in a clear, unaffected voice, "Welcome to Strassburg, Monsieur. I hope you will visit us often." There was nothing extraordinary about the greeting, but, quite abruptly, he found his behavior taking the strangest turns.

Try as he might, he could not concentrate on the conversation round the dinner table. Nor could he taste the food he ate so mechanically. For some odd reason, his gaze insisted on returning again and again to the girl who sat behind the silver candlesticks. She was slender, and wore a simple dark gown that matched the color of her eyes. Her face was a smooth-complexioned oval, her chin firm, her eyebrows prominent and finely arched. Her hair was

parted in the middle and swept down over her ears. She
sat erect, gesturing with small hands when she talked. Her
manner was gentle, direct and, to Louis, fascinating; so
fascinating, indeed, that he did not hear his host ask him
a question about his planned work at Strassburg.

"Louis," Pierre called innocently, "Monsieur Laurent is
speaking to you."

Louis' eyes jumped to the end of the table. He saw
Pierre's wise, almost mocking expression. Madame Laurent
lowered her gaze to her plate in an effort to conceal her
smile. Blood rose in Louis' face. He blinked.

"I'm sorry, Monsieur. My mind was elsewhere."

"So I see," Laurent observed dryly.

Walking home later along deserted streets, Bertin pounded
his friend's shoulder and chortled at the sky, "I think the
impossible has happened. The genius Pasteur has been
smitten by a very young and a very beautiful lady!"

"Don't talk nonsense!" Louis demanded impatiently.

But, in the next days, he wondered if Pierre hadn't spoken
the truth. His conscientious mind simply refused to behave
conscientiously. Experiments were far from complete by
nightfall because he had spent so much time thinking of
Marie's voice and smile. Her face even came to him while
he was in class and chased his well-prepared lectures right
out the window.

He invented all sorts of excuses to visit the Laurent
home nightly—a question to ask the Rector about the university, a little gift to repay Madame Laurent's hospitality,
a book to borrow and then return. But the knowing glances
exchanged by Monsieur and Madame Laurent told him he
wasn't fooling them one bit.

He had been at Strassburg less than a month when he realized he wanted to marry Marie. It was a custom of the day that a young man write the father of his prospective bride for permission to wed. Louis wrote such a letter on February 10, 1849. In it he described his family background, financial status, and future prospects. He concluded with the words, "My father will come to Strassburg to make this proposal of marriage."

Then began the agony of waiting for a reply. Monsieur Laurent's answer was long in coming and Louis' work suffered badly. At times, he was absolutely certain the Rector would never accept him as a son-in-law. The Laurent family was higher socially than his, and he was sure his appearance just wasn't fine enough for Marie. He was too short, his nose too broad, and his eyes too somber. Such was his remorse one day that he wrote Madame Laurent, "I am afraid Mlle. Marie may be influenced by early impressions not favorable to me. I know there is nothing in me to attract a young girl's fancy. But I do know that those who have known me very well have loved me very much."

But at last came the day when his spirits soared. Permission for the marriage was granted. Louis' father and his sister, Josephine, came to Strassburg to arrange the final details of the wedding, which took place on May 29, 1849.

With his future settled, Louis couldn't resist his work. On the morning of the wedding he was missing! "I can guess where he is," said a highly nervous Pierre Bertin, who then hurried to the university laboratory to drag him from an experiment.

The next five years were the happiest in the young scientist's life. Later would come the scientific battles and personal tragedies that would leave him ill and exhausted. But, from 1849 to 1854, he lived in almost perfect peace. Marie proved to be the finest wife he could have found. She guarded his health zealously. She saw that he missed no meals and got sufficient sleep. Though she had to care for the three children—Jeanne, Jean-Baptiste, and Cécile—born to them during these years, Marie took an active interest in Louis' work. She visited her husband's lab often and listened to him talk endlessly of experiments she really did not quite understand. Very early in their marriage she adopted the life-long habit of copying his notes every evening in a neat hand.

Louis experienced both disappointment and triumph in his work at this time. His crystal studies had convinced him that the very life of substances could be changed by altering the positions of their molecules. He tried to change the life of plants by placing them between huge magnets and by swinging them back and forth across the lab at the ends of giant pendulums. These experiments failed.

But not so his attempt to manufacture racemic acid. It was the true paratartaric acid and one of the mysteries of chemistry. It had been discovered in 1820 by a man named Kestner while he was manufacturing tartaric acid. But, elusive thing that it was, it soon ceased to appear, and chemists throughout Europe failed in every attempt to produce it. The Pharmaceutical Society of Paris offered a prize of 1,500 francs to the scientist who succeeded in manufacturing the rare acid artificially.

Louis was convinced racemic acid could be found hidden in the tartaric acids. He spent every vacation traveling through Europe, studying various tartars in Prague, Leipzig, and Vienna. Often he did find traces of the stuff in the tartars, but only mere traces, not enough to be of service to any chemist. On other occasions, he was told by scientists that they had long been able to produce the fleeting liquid. Without exception, he found that each had mistaken another substance for it. It remained for him, after constant and discouraging experimentation, to manufacture the rare acid in his own lab at Strassburg. This was accomplished in 1853 by keeping cinchonine acid at a high temperature for several hours.

His achievement won for him the prize offered by the Pharmaceutical Society. Half the money he donated for student laboratories at Strassburg, investing the remaining half in his own work.

Causing him even greater pride was the award of the red ribbon of the Legion of Honor for his feat. It seemed as if he had barely received these tributes—actually eighteen months had passed—when he dashed into his house on the Rue des Couples more excited than usual and embraced Marie.

"I've splendid news for you! A grand surprise! We're moving to Lille!"

He thoroughly enjoyed his wife's look of astonishment. "But why?"

"Because I've been appointed Professor and Dean of the new school of science at the university there!"

He held her at arm's length and saw her glance about her beloved living room. In her eyes was the pain a woman always feels when she is torn from familiar surroundings.

His own expression sobered. "I'm sorry, my dear. I thought you would be happy."

Then he was smiling again, seeing the quick brightening

of her face. "But I am, Louis. You've taken a wonderful step forward and I'm very proud of you. When do we leave?"

"Immediately!" He began to stride about the room, envisioning all the furnishings and silver and dishware in packing boxes. "Ah, there's so much to do!"

And so began the move that was to bring him into contact with the invisible giants, the giants that would give his name to the ages.

CHAPTER

5

The First of
the Giants

"We have a dream here at the university. Lille
is one of the greatest manufacturing centers in France. We
want our new science school to help our industry become
even greater."

Those words of the head of Lille University were spoken
to Louis in September of 1854. They sounded thrilling in
the ears of the thirty-two-year-old professor and he heard
himself reply:

"I'll do my best to make the dream a reality."

"As head of the science school, you will have the respon-
sibility of acquainting the townspeople with the many services science can render their factories. A union between
science and industry—that's what we want."

Louis' eyes sparkled. He thrust his newly grown beard
forward. A union between science and industry! He liked
the men of Lille University. Their idea was worth fighting
for—a real challenge.

He devoted himself wholeheartedly to this challenge during the next months while Marie settled the family into their new home. He addressed any gathering that would hear him and struggled to ignite what sometimes proved to be dull imaginations with word pictures such as: "Where in your families will you find a young man whose curiosity and interest will not immediately be awakened when you put into his hands a potato, when with that potato he may produce sugar, with that sugar alcohol, with that alcohol ether and vinegar? Where is he who will not be happy to tell his family in the evening that he has just been working out an electric telegraph?"

He took special delight in his classes. The university wanted the students to receive practical scientific training that would aid them later in the factories and distilleries of the area. Louis saw to it that they got that training. He established laboratory classes and awarded a diploma at the end of two years that qualified its holder for the position of factory foreman. He refused to limit his work to the classroom and lab. He took his pupils on tours of factories, iron foundries, and steel and metal works at Aniche, Valenciennes, St. Omer, and Denain, even venturing as far north as Belgium in 1856. He made his young charges question workers and foremen about every phase of their work. These young people would know their business when he was done with them. Of that he was certain!

He searched endlessly for interesting lecture material and that search brought him to the subject that was to fascinate him for the rest of his days and create for him enemies and friends throughout the world. He spoke of it to Marie and the children one day at lunch.

"Tomorrow I'm going to lecture on the most interesting creatures on earth."

"And they are?"

"Little germs so small they cannot be seen by the naked eye."

A soprano laugh erupted at his side. "Oh, papa, are there really such things?" Jeanne, little more than five and as dark haired as her mother, asked.

"Yes, indeed. I believe they live everywhere—in the air we breathe and the food and water we consume."

Jeanne stared at her plate. Her only comment was a humorous "Ugh!"

Four-year-old Jean-Baptiste investigated with a serious, puckered face a bit of potato on his fork. He turned the fork slowly. "I don't see them," he announced.

Only Cécile, age two, took no interest in the conversation. Her attention was held by a bird on the window sill.

"Of course you don't see them, Jean," Louis smiled. "As I said, they're so small they can't be seen without the aid of a microscope. But they're there, nevertheless, these wee germs." He used a term by which he was often to call them for some time to come. In future years, science would give these infinitesimal plants and animals a wide variety of names—names such as microbes and micro-organisms. Some names, among them bacteria, bacilli, and virus, would depend on the nature of the tiny beings.

"Science has known about these little things for centuries," Louis explained. "The ancient Greeks saw them. And so did the Dutchman, Antony Leeuwenhoek, a century and a half ago in the first of the microscopes he invented. There they were, countless numbers of them swimming in water, and he called them 'animacules.' The Italian priest and scientist, Pere Spallanzani, sighted them again in the 1700s. And recently Doctor Schwann of Germany saw them by the millions in aged meat. There's no telling how important they may be to the world."

He gazed round the table at the rapt faces of his family. Even Cécile was watching him, for the bird had gone. She didn't understand him, but the vibrancy in his voice told her he was saying something important. Suddenly he frowned and his tone grew angry.

"But most scientists today pay no attention to them! They claim they are too small to be of any value. Imagine! They laugh and call them mere curiosities! But, fortunately, there are other scientists—too few, I'm sorry to say—who believe these infinitesimal creatures are giant forces for good and evil in this world. And I'm proud to think I've joined them."

A knock sounded at the door, interrupting his flow of words. Marie put her napkin aside and left the room. When she returned, her face was troubled.

"There's a Monsieur Bigo to see you. He says his son is a student in one of your classes."

"Yes. I know the boy well. What does Monsieur Bigo want?"

Marie shook her head. "He didn't say. But I think you should see him immediately. He seems very upset and I'm sure he's in some sort of trouble."

Louis found Monsieur Bigo bobbing up and down on the toes of his well-polished shoes before the living-room fireplace. He was middle aged, portly, and red faced. He greeted Louis with a wagging bald head and extended his hand.

"Professor Pasteur. It is a pleasure to meet you. My son speaks of you constantly."

"Thank you. He's a fine student."

Louis gestured his visitor to a chair. Bigo sat far forward in the chair, clasping and unclasping his hands. He cleared his throat nervously. "My son tells me you have lectured in class on the subject of fermentation."

Louis nodded. He recalled that just last week he had explained to his students that fermentation was the name given nature's method of changing certain elements in many substances into alcohol or acid. "I find it an interesting subject. I've often wondered what causes it."

"Good! Then you are the man for me."

"I'm afraid I don't understand."

"Let me explain. I am a distiller. I manufacture alcohol from sugar beets. My distillery is one of the finest—if not the finest—in Lille. It has been in the family for generations." Bigo straightened proudly. Had he been a peacock he would have ruffled his plumage. Quite suddenly, his face clouded again. "But I'm being ruined, driven into bankruptcy by bad fermentations that produce a rotten liquid instead of alcohol."

"I see."

"I am not the only distiller with this difficulty. There are others, all of them being ruined. But my son tells me of this genius Pasteur. And I say to myself: I will go to him and he will help me."

Louis held up his hand. "One moment, Monsieur. Am I to understand you wish me to cure your bad fermentations?"

Bigo wagged his head vigorously. Beads of perspiration stood out on his forehead. "Precisely. Help me, Professor. I implore you. Help all the distillers of Lille."

"Monsieur," Louis objected gently, "I am interested in the subject and I have read in the newspapers of the troubles the distillers are having. The students talk often of them. But I know very little of the fermentation process. My major interest is crystallography."

"Bah! So you say you know very little? You will learn. And you will solve our problem and prove to the entire city that you really mean your fine words about science helping industry." Bigo was bouncing again, his pudgy hands gesticulating furiously. "Yes, you will learn. My son says you can do anything. You have no idea how he talks about you. The great Pasteur this and the great Pasteur that. . . ."

Louis sheltered a smile behind his hand. The flow of words reminded him of Balard with the Minister of Education almost ten years ago. The minister hadn't been able to withstand the verbal torrent. Well, neither could he.

"All right, Monsieur. I'll look into your problem. My greatest desire is to show Lille industry the services science can render it," he said. "But, mind you, I promise only to look into the problem. I know so little of fermentations. I cannot promise a solution."

"But you will find the solution. I know you will. You are very clever. My son says—"

"I appreciate your son's regard for me, but I am not really as clever as I would sometimes like to think," Louis said, rising. "When may I come to your distillery to obtain samples of your fermentations?"

"Whenever you wish. My entire establishment is at your disposal."

"I think I should like to come immediately."

"Immediately? Right now? Today?" Bigo's eyes widened. "You are willing to drop your other work this instant?"

"Yes. I'm free from classes this afternoon," Louis said,

moving to the kitchen to collect several small bottles and place them in a valise. Now that he had accepted the task he was eager to get at it, eager to go chasing after the mysterious, the unknown.

"At least you can finish your lunch," Marie protested. She knew full well she was wasting her breath.

"I'm afraid not, my dear," were his last words to her as he disappeared out the front door, his hat absent-mindedly thrust down on his head at a careless angle. "The fermentations simply won't wait that long!"

Riding across town in Monsieur Bigo's carriage, he had no eyes for the passing scenery, the strollers enjoying the afternoon sun, the trees heavy with foliage, the parks a thick carpet of green. He was taken up completely with recalling to mind what he had learned of fermentation while preparing his class lectures.

It was a mystery as old as mankind itself. First, as he had told his students, it was the process by which nature caused certain elements in substances to slowly change into alcohol and acids. There were many different types of fermentation. Chief among them was "alcoholic fermentation," meaning the production of alcohol for wines and beers from the sugar or starch in things such as grapes, beets, wheat, barley and corn. The souring of milk, converting milk sugar into lactic acid, was called "lactic acid fermentation," and the term applied to the change of wine into cider or vinegar was "acetic acid fermentation."

Though scientists had been able to identify the various types of fermentation, they really knew nothing at the time of *how* and *why* the process took place at all. They knew that, in alcoholic fermentation, yeast had to be added to things being fermented before alcohol would appear. But what actually occurred after the yeast was added—well, that was anybody's guess.

"And the guesses are many," Louis sighed inwardly. "Most scientists believe alcoholic fermentation—as well as all others—is caused by chemical action."

The guess that had earned the greatest following was that of Justus von Liebig, the famous German biochemist. He believed the yeasts died, releasing an albuminous material that set the sugar molecules to vibrating and broke them down into carbon dioxide and alcohol.

Louis now recalled a story that linked alcoholic fermentation to the "wee germs" that so fascinated him. It was the story of the French chemist, Cagniard de la Tour. Nearly twenty years ago, in 1837, de la Tour had studied the little yeast globules that turn barley into alcohol. Looking into his microscope, he had seen the globules sprout tiny buds along their sides. Then he had watched the tiny buds break away and, becoming globules themselves, go swimming off to sprout buds of their own. The yeasts had multiplied themselves a thousand times over in this manner and had convinced de la Tour that they were living things. He had wasted no time in concluding that these living things, not chemical action, were responsible for fermentation. Later, Frederich Kutzing and Theodor Schwann, who had performed similar experiments, supported his view.

Louis shook his head bitterly. "But de la Tour was not a well known man. Apparently very few heard of his discovery, and those who did preferred to forget it. They put it on a shelf and got it out of mind because they couldn't stand new ideas," he told himself. "It's not just! This man did much to reveal the possible cause of fermentation and he has gone ignored all these years. When are all our tight-minded scientists going to learn to appreciate the little germs?"

A pudgy hand touched Louis' knee. "We've arrived, Professor," Monsieur Bigo said.

Louis came out of his reverie to see that the carriage had entered the industrial section of town and had halted before the Bigo distillery. It was a large frame warehouse with a loading ramp running along one wall. Inside were the giant fermenting vats.

Bigo's son met them on the loading ramp. He was a slender, good looking youth whom Louis knew to be a better-than-average student. The boy gripped his hand happily.

"Professor! I knew you'd help us."

Louis followed father and son into the dimly lighted warehouse. A sharp, tangy odor accosted him.

"First, we'll see the beets that have gone bad," Bigo announced, leading the scientist to a nearby vat and pointing. "Look. Terrible, isn't it?"

Louis grimaced. The little distiller had spoken the truth. The vat was filled with a slimy, grayish substance from which came a foul odor.

"The financial loss my father has suffered from this one vat," young Bigo said angrily, "would bankrupt the average man. The entire distilling industry is being ruined."

Louis took a bottle from his valise. He rolled up his sleeve and, setting his mouth in a hard line, leaned far over the rim of the vat. He heard Bigo cry, "No, no, Professor. It's filthy stuff. Let me do that for you."

"No need," Louis murmured from between compressed

lips. He dipped his hand into the grayish sea. A thick, lumpy coldness squeezed his wrists. In truth, he detested this moment. He had always hated ugliness. But he had learned long ago that he must be ready to endure filth of any sort for his work.

Seconds later, the bottle was filled with a specimen of the unhealthy beet juice.

Then, within five minutes, Louis had removed a specimen from a properly functioning vat. The liquid in this container pleased him. It was foamy at the top and clear and darkish beneath.

"Now," he said, "I must take these samples to my lab and learn all I can from them."

"I wish you good fortune. My carriage will return you to the university," Monsieur Bigo said. He added, with a pomposity that made Louis smile, "I am sure the fate of my entire distillery rides with you."

Young Bigo asked shyly, "May I accompany you, Professor?"

"Of course. Who knows? Someday, when this distillery passes into your hands, you may put to use what we learn this afternoon—if we learn anything at all. Remember, Monsieur Bigo, I may not be able to solve your problem."

Louis thought the ride to the university would last forever. His hands ran over the valise and he could hardly wait to get to his microscope. Who knew what the contents of the little bottles would show him? Perhaps one of the secrets of fermentation. Perhaps nothing. This was the real adventure of science—not knowing what the next minute, the next second, would show you of nature and her endless mysteries.

The carriage finally halted and he was able to enter his

laboratory. He gave the place not a single critical glance to-day. He didn't even stop to begrudge the fact that his microscope was the crudest of instruments. He thought only of removing the bottles from the valise and getting to work.

Young Bigo stood at his shoulder as he put several drops of the healthy fluid on a small glass rectangle and placed it on the microscope stage. He bent over the instrument.

Nothing greeted his eye but a circle of harsh yellow-white light. He focused the lens below the eyepiece.

"Ah!"

He sighed unconsciously, for suddenly a whole world filled the bright circle—a world of violent, churning activity; a world increased a thousand times beyond its actual size; a world that only men of the microscope were privileged to see.

His breath came quickly. Hundreds, perhaps thousands, of tiny things wiggled and cavorted in the yellow-white circle. They looked like tiny circles, or globules. Alone, in confused groups and in long, swaying chains, they danced and twisted, silently, aimlessly, unaware of the Cyclopean eye that followed their every busy movement.

He chuckled delightedly, recognizing them. They were the little yeasts de la Tour had seen.

"What's this?"

His back stiffened. His heart thudded suddenly.

Young Bigo moved excitedly at his side. "What is it, Professor? What is it?"

"Look for yourself."

Louis hastily stepped aside and the student lowered his eyes to the instrument. The scientist peered at him eagerly. "All over the circle, my boy! See what's happening? Little buds sprout out along the sides of the yeast globules. See them? They look like infinitesimal plants. Give them time and you'll see them break away from the yeasts and swim off all by themselves."

"Yes, yes, I see them. They seem to grow right out of the yeasts," young Bigo said in astonishment. He raised bewildered eyes. "But I don't understand. What does this mean?"

"Remember my class lectures on Cagniard de la Tour, Kutzing, and Schwann, and you'll realize what it means. With our own eyes, we've just seen that they were right when they said yeasts are living things. We've watched the yeasts growing their young."

Louis strode the length of the room. His beard was against his chest, one hand behind his back, the other gesturing carelessly. "De la Tour claimed that living things—not chemical action—are responsible for fermentations. What a thing that would be to prove! What a blow all the smug and old-fashioned scientists who snicker at the importance of these tiny beings would suffer!"

He stopped before young Bigo. His eyes were shining. "Mark my words, when science recognizes the importance of the wee germs, it will make great strides forward. Great new avenues for study will be opened—"

He checked the rising tide of his imagination. "But that is for the future. Your father's problem is the matter at hand."

He gripped the bottle of gray fluid and held it up to the light.

"Now let us see what our unhealthy specimen has to show us."

The Battle of the
Fermentations

Into the microscope went a smear of the unhealthy specimen and, almost instantly, Louis' excitement vanished. His hand crawled through his hair in confusion. The sample revealed itself to be nothing but a solid mass of gray. There was no sign of life in it. Nor was a single yeast globule visible.

He forgot young Bigo entirely as he sniffed at specimen bottle, revolted by its stench. He put a drop of the gray substance on the tip of his tongue. There was sourness in the odor and taste of the stuff. He inserted narrow strips of blue litmus paper into the bottle and watched them turn red.

"There's acid here, lactic acid, and that shouldn't be present in an alcoholic fermentation," he murmured.

Young Bigo's voice seemed to come from a great distance. "What's happened to all the yeasts?"

"I don't know." He was talking as much to himself as to the boy. "Perhaps they've been killed."

He picked up the bottle and young Bigo was forgotten again. He sat motionless, eyebrows flat, head set low against hunched shoulders. Only his eyes were alive. They were hard and bright and unblinking, as if, by their very ferocity, they hoped to wrest from the evil-smelling liquid its deepest secrets. Outside, the sky turned red with the lowering sun, then purpled as the long summer dusk came upon Lille. Young Bigo departed, his good-bye call unheard. Louis turned the bottle slowly in his hands. He watched the fluid roll and cloud and deposit tiny specks of gray matter on the glass walls. . . .

Tiny specks of gray matter!

Why, he hadn't noticed them before.

Had he really seen them?

Yes. Yes. There they were, clinging to the sides and bottom of the bottle. Some of them even floated lazily on the surface of the liquid. Had they just appeared or had they been there all the while? He could have missed them quite easily. The light was very poor in the lab. He shook the bottle. The fluid clouded. When it cleared, the specks were still there, almost invisible, but still there.

Carefully, so very carefully, he inserted a thin glass tube into the bottle and transferred one of the minute things to the microscope. What he saw made it impossible for him to raise his head from the eyepiece. The speck, now highly magnified, had become a disorderly army of twisting germs. Like the yeast globules, some of them wobbled and skittered about alone, while others clung together in clusters and chains. But there the similarity ended. The yeasts had been round; these fellows were shaped like slightly curved rods, like the tiniest sausages man had ever seen. Too, they were much smaller than the yeasts, each about twenty-five thou-sandths of an inch long.

From that moment on, Louis thought of nothing but the little rod-like creatures. His every instinct whispered that they had brought him to the threshold of some great discovery. Just what, he could not say. But that didn't matter. His only concern was to learn all he could about them. He returned time and again to Monsieur Bigo's distillery to obtain additional specimens. He missed so many meals that Marie lost patience with him. Monsieur Bigo became short tempered, exclaiming at last to his son,

"This great Pasteur of yours! Bah! He's completely for-gotten our problem. He thinks only of his germs. Little rods, he calls them. Do you know what happened today! I met him by one of the vats and asked him if he had found any remedy for our bad fermentations." The distiller slapped his forehead and glanced heavenward. "He looked at me as if he didn't know what I was talking about!"

"Be patient, Father, please," young Bigo implored. "Granted, the Professor seems to have forgotten you, but, take my word for it, his studies may someday profit *all* French distillers."

The boy spoke with authority, for he worked at Louis' side constantly during these days. He watched the chemist examine endless specimens, watched him compare filtered with nonfiltered beetroot juice, watched him scribble many theories in his notebook, and watched him savagely write "error" over all those that later experiments proved in-correct. And he heard Louis tell him one day,

"The microscope has shown us that the globules are quite round when fermentation is healthy. They lengthen when it begins to sicken. When it is completely bad the little rods are present. They're the villains. If your father will keep them out of his vats, he'll have no more difficulty."

"But how will he do this?"

Louis had to admit he did not know. But his disappointment at being unable to help Monsieur Bigo could not long prevail, for his studies had given him an idea that set his spine to tingling. If it proved itself correct, it would solve the age-old mystery of fermentation and revolutionize chemistry. He mulled over it daily. He was certain it was the discovery he had felt at hand when first he had seen the little rods, and he knew he must soon speak of it to another scientist.

An opportunity to test its merits on the ears of the finest scientist of them all, the beloved Biot, came unexpectedly in early 1857. The old man, with Balard, Dumas, and the chemist Senarmont, wrote him to come to Paris immediately to try to gain a recently vacated seat in the mineralogy section of the Academy of Sciences. Louis journeyed north with misgiving. The vacancy would be filled through an election by Academy members and, knowing he was not cut out for political campaigning, he was certain he would not obtain the thirty votes necessary for the seat. His fears were well grounded. Though Senarmont informed the Academy that Louis' work in crystallography had just won him the Rumford Medal from the Royal Society in London, he managed to obtain but a disappointing sixteen votes in March of 1857.

But his talk with Biot made the entire Paris venture worthwhile. It took place at the old man's rooms the day before Louis' return to Lille. Biot welcomed him with an embrace, and Louis, as he had been since coming to Paris, was shocked by what time had done to this man who had come to look on him as a son. The scientist was now eighty-four, his face haggard and colorless. Deep lines scored his hollowing cheeks and veins webbed that giant, bony nose. But his eyes, red rimmed, remained the burning, penetrating things they had always been.

He took Louis to chairs in front of a fireplace. "I can't tell you how sorry I am you were refused by the Academy," he said in a hoarse whisper. "But take heart. Your day will yet come."

Louis nodded his gratitude while Biot, with much sighing, deposited himself in a chair. When Louis had seated himself opposite, the ancient face smiled wisely. "But you didn't come here to sorrow about the Academy. That's all past. You want to get something off your mind. You've wanted to get it off your mind since the day you arrived in Paris. I've sensed it."

"That's very true. But I haven't had the time until now."

Biot's eyes glittered. "Something about your work?"

"Yes."

"Excellent." Biot settled his chin in an upraised hand. There was not a trace of his skepticism of a decade ago in his manner now. His attitude was one of silent attention. "Well, let's hear it."

Louis slowly outlined his studies of the past months. He watched the old man nod approvingly from time to time. At last he was ready to put into words his grand idea. "As we all know, yeasts cause sugar in the beets to ferment into alcohol. But somehow the little rods get into the beets—perhaps from the air. They kill the yeasts and seem to make the fermentations go bad. But, in reality, they are causing *another* type of fermentation—the change of the sugar into lactic acid."

"I agree."

"Both the yeasts and the rods are alive," Louis continued. "Now my idea is this: is it possible that *all* fermentations are caused by living things—and that each substance to be fermented requires a *special living thing all its own* to do the job? Yeasts to make alcohol. Another type of germ to cause milk to sour and produce lactic acid. And another type to produce vinegar from cider. And still other germs to make other things, such as butyric acid. . . ."

Biot's hand struck the arm of his chair and his cackling laugh went round the walls. "My boy, you have a genuine talent for concocting right out of thin air the most uncanny theories. *Living ferments and a specific ferment for each substance to be changed!* It could be the answer to the whole secret of the cause of fermentation."

Suddenly his eyes were somber. "But it's an idea that's going to bring you trouble. You'll be challenged and scorned by every chemist who belittles the little germs you think so important."

"I'm ready for them," Louis said defiantly.

"And you'll have to fight the very popular theory that fermentations are caused by chemical action."

"I'm ready for that, too."

"Good. What steps do you plan to take to prove your theory?"

"I'm going to check every substance that can be fermented and see if living things are always present and responsible for the change," Louis said. "I intend to start with lactic acid fermentation—the souring of milk."

Biot sat far back in his chair, digesting this information. "Excellent. Excellent," he sighed. "Ever since the day you first brought me your crystals, your work has given me much pleasure. In you, I see myself as I was so many years ago. And now this work you plan—it is more than I ever hoped for."

The old man lifted himself to his feet. He looked little more than a living skeleton as he moved to a nearby table. He took a package from the table and extended it to the young scientist. "I have a gift for you to take back to Lille."

Quickly, Louis undid the wrappings and found himself looking at a photograph of Biot. It had been taken in the laboratory of the chemist Henri Renault, and revealed Biot seated at a work table. His shoulders were stooped and the tiredness in his aged body was painfully evident. But the familiar luster, the fire, was in his eyes as usual.

After he had left the apartment, Louis felt a bit foolish. He had been so moved that he had been almost unable to thank the old man and had stumbled blindly from the rooms like an awkward schoolboy.

Back at Lille, with Biot's faith to bolster him, he immediately launched his study of souring milk. "I hope it will prove a simple task," he confided in Marie. "This lactic acid fermentation itself is the simplest of the lot. Basically, it is the breakdown of the sugar molecule into two halves. Those two halves are the lactic acid molecules. If only I can prove living beings cause that breakdown!"

The study *did* appear simple in its beginning stages. He soon came upon patches of gray material in his bottles of souring milk. He found them so easy to confuse with other products of lactic acid fermentation that he knew it was no wonder chemists and naturalists had failed to notice them before. He studied them in the microscope, learned that they were composed of minute globules, infinitely smaller than the yeast globules. Into his notebook went endless drawings of these tiny creatures. He was certain they were the cause of lactic acid fermentation.

His little daughter, Jeanne, was in the habit of accompanying her mother on frequent visits to the lab. On one such occasion, he showed her the little globules and said, "They are very much alive. I've seen them moving and growing their young. Now I must see them actually produce lactic acid."

She regarded with serious eyes the bottles on the work bench. "But how can you see them do anything? This liquid is so dirty looking."

"Well!" he thought, "what is the saying about truth coming from the mouths of babes?" He stroked his beard pompously and said, "Ah, Doctor Scientist, you have touched on the very problem that has been bothering me for days."

The little girl squealed delightedly. Dark braids skipped about her shoulders. It was good to see Papa full of fun. Usually, when he was doing some sort of old experiment he was so serious, and sometimes he didn't even seem to hear you when you talked to him. She made her tone as pompous as his. "Well, what are you going to do about this, Monsieur Professor?"

Louis winked. "Cook a soup."

"Oh, Papa, now you're fooling me too much."

On the contrary, he wasn't fooling one bit. A soup was exactly what he needed; a clear broth in which he could see the globules growing and causing fermentation. It was absolutely necessary if he was to prove his theory. But exactly what sort of broth would he cook? He had pondered that question for days.

And he pondered it and experimented with it for long days to come. It was discouraging labor. The little globules were particular fellows. So often, after he had painstakingly concocted a new soup, they would decide they didn't like it and would die, causing his spirits to sink low and causing him to wrack his brain for ideas for yet another bouillon.

Then, one day, when he suspected he was just about out of ideas, he mixed exact amounts of carbonate of chalk and a boiled albuminous matter in a sugar solution. He cast a trace of the little globules into this last-resort concoction and shoved it into an incubator.

He stepped back. He could do no more. He must wait until tomorrow to learn if the globules lived or died. He was tired, but he didn't sleep well that night. He tossed and turned and murmured repeatedly, "The broth has to work. If it doesn't, I don't know where to turn next."

But, by late afternoon of the following day, he knew he had to search no further, for fermentation was beginning to take place in the container of solution. There was no doubt of it! The liquid was clouded and bubbles rose from its depths to burst on the surface.

He looked at several drops of the liquid in his microscope and promptly forgot what time it was and the fact that his dinner would soon be waiting for him. Just below his eye were the little globules. They were alive and as healthy as he could desire. How they twisted and danced for him! And now they multiplied!

Back to the container he went. The bubbles were rising more quickly now. The cloudiness had thickened. Good!

Both were signs the globules were increasing in number as the fermentation progressed.

He waited patiently until the process had been completed and the solution had evaporated. Then he scrutinized every single bit of matter remaining in the dish. "Perfect! Perfect!" he exclaimed. "The sugar has been transformed into carbon dioxide and lactic acid. The lactic acid has combined with the carbonate of chalk and has crystallized."

He slapped the work bench triumphantly. Not only had his clear broth shown him that the germs were alive as fermentation took place but that *as they had multiplied the process had quickened its speed!* Both facts indicated they had caused the whole thing to happen. Now he would make absolutely certain of this.

He spent the next weeks concocting the brew again and again and experimenting with it. The results of these experiments were exactly what he had hoped they would be:

1. Fermentation occurred only when the little globules were on hand.

2. Fermentation progressed slowly when only a few globules were present.

3. But it quickened when more globules were added. The more the merrier. The greatest number of globules always meant the fastest fermentation.

There! The job was done. All traces of doubt were removed. Lactic acid fermentation depended entirely on the tiny germs. "In this one case, at least, I've proved my theory on both counts," Louis exulted. "Living things caused it. And the globules, altogether different from those of yeast in alcoholic fermentation, show that lactic acid requires a specific ferment all its own."

Now the tight-minded scientists would have to admit what mighty work the "wee germs"—those tiny, invisible giants—performed in nature. Louis wrote a fifteen page report on his findings and submitted it to the Lille Scientific Society. Three months later it was sent to the Academy of Sciences in Paris where it ignited a great controversy.

"Good for Pasteur," some of the members cried. "This is the answer to the cause of *all* fermentations."

"Not so fast," others retorted. "He's made an error somewhere. Chemical action, not stupid little bugs, produces fermentation. The great Liebig says so. All the best brains in Europe say so. How dare this young upstart try to prove them wrong!"

This was the first of many public battles that were to surround the bearded scientist for the rest of his days.

But he paid little attention to the clamor. He was too busy tracking down the germs responsible for other fermentations. This detective work, lasting several years, uncovered the micro-organisms responsible for butyric and acetic acid fermentations.

Soon he was telling his family, "Each one of these germs is a living organism. Each type has its own individual shape and structure. You cannot feed them all the same food. Each requires its own special diet, and fermentation will not take place if they are unhealthy or absent."

In the autumn of 1857, when he was thirty-five years old, he had other good news for his family. He extended a letter, written on very important looking stationery, to Marie and the children. "Here's our passport back to Paris! It's from the Minister of Education. He wants me to become Director of Scientific Studies at the École Normale!"

Marie gripped his hands. "Louis, how wonderful! It's a great honor. You're going to accept, of course?"

"But of course," he replied, laughing. "I'm much attached to Lille and I shall hate leaving my lab, small as it is, but I can't ignore the opportunity to get back to Paris. Such wonderful things in science are happening there."

Reluctantly, the University of Lille accepted his resignation. The Rector heralded his departure with the words, "Our faculty loses a professor and a scientist of the first order."

Biot, leaning heavily on a cane, greeted Louis in Paris with the disquieting words, "You should have remained in Lille. At least you had a lab there. That's more than the École Normale will be able to give you."

"But surely the school will have some sort of work space for me."

"No, it won't! There just isn't any space." Biot thumped the floor with his cane and explained that, since Balard had left to teach at the Collège de France, the only lab in the École Normale was occupied by his successor, Henri Saint Claire Deville. "It's not even fit for mice! It's dark and cold, and his equipment is so poor that I want to destroy it. But, poor fellow, he does the best he can with it."

Louis was quiet for a moment. When he spoke again, his voice was flat with determination. "If the school won't give me a lab, then I shall have to find one for myself."

Biot snorted. "And what will you find? Probably a miserable garret. Your fate will be the same as that of your good friend, Auguste Laurent. He had to work in a cold cellar that destroyed his health and brought about his death years before his time."

Biot's prediction about a garret came true. With Marie at his side, Louis searched the entire building on the Rue d'Ulm for suitable quarters. At the end of the week, he shrugged ruefully. "There's only one place we haven't looked—the attic."

Marie tried to smile encouragingly. "Shall we go up?"

They ascended rickety stairs and came upon two small, low-ceilinged rooms. Dirty windows grayed the sunlight. Dust mantled odds and ends of cast-off furniture and school equipment. The floor sagged underfoot.

"If cleaned, it might do," Louis said. He tugged his beard. "In fact, it will have to do."

"But you'll roast to death in summer," Marie protested, "and freeze in the winter."

Nevertheless, Louis cheerfully got at the job of turning the grim rooms into a laboratory. Having no assistant, he himself cleaned the place and installed his equipment. He assured himself with a wry smile that his new quarters wouldn't be bad at all—"Even if the floor is likely to collapse momentarily."

A long parade of tasks filled his days as he struggled to ready his garret lab. There were lectures and demonstrations to prepare, and new students to meet. As Dean, he had to order food for the school and see that workmen kept the building in good repair. His notebook became pocked with such reminders as, "Courtyard to be strewn with sand . . . Ventilation of classrooms . . . Dining hall door to be repaired." His conscientious nature would not allow him to overlook a single detail.

These time-consuming responsibilities and the birth of his fourth child—a daughter, Marie-Louise—in 1858 kept his mind from the fermentation studies for a long while. But at last he got back to work. News of his recent findings had reached Germany and out of that country came the angry rumblings of Justus von Liebig, the leading exponent of the theory of fermentation by chemical action. His proud scientific feathers badly ruffled, the chemist stubbornly refused to believe Pasteur's "wee germs" had anything to do with the process. He centered his arguments about the all-important alcoholic fermentation.

"I have always said and I will always say," he announced, "that alcoholic fermentation occurs only after the yeasts have died. Upon their death, they decompose and give off an albuminous material which is the real cause of fermentation. It sets the sugar molecules to vibrating and breaks them down into carbon dioxide and alcohol."

He went on to stress a new proof of the death of the yeasts. "Louis Thenard has recently found that the weight of yeast decreases during fermentation. This means there are fewer yeast globules alive at the end of the process than at its beginning. Thenard has proved once and for all that the yeasts *do* die."

Louis bristled. This Liebig needed to be answered—and answered promptly. "If I don't prove his ideas wrong," Louis told Marie, "science will never recognize the importance of the little germs."

"And just how do you plan to prove him wrong?"

He shrugged elaborately. "I shall become a chef again. I concocted a broth in which I could see the globules producing lactic acid. Now a broth must be found in which I can see the yeasts producing alcohol."

Though he spoke lightly, he set about his task in dead earnest. He realized this was the final battle of the fermentations, and, as the year 1857 moved into December, he also realized he was living the lactic acid experiment all over again. The proper recipe for this new soup was as hard to create as had been that for the lactic acid globules.

But it *had* to be found and it *was* found. And what a strange brew it turned out to be—a mixture of sugar, water, mineral salts, ammonia, potassium, magnesium, and iron. But it worked. Oh, how it worked! It succeeded beyond his fondest hopes.

Dizzy with exhaustion, he half-ran and half-staggered home one night to tell Marie, "My dear, I've put the yeasts into the soup so many times that I simply can't do it again! The results match those of the lactic acid study exactly. The yeast germs don't die. I think Thenard and Liebig must have seen them die because of some contaminating bacteria in their solutions. But I've seen them live and multiply. And I've come to know that the faster they multiply and the stronger they are the faster fermentation takes place. Everything I've seen adds up to the fact that they're responsible for the whole process!"

Liebig had also said that the yeasts give off ammonia while decomposing. Louis' experiment proved that, instead of releasing ammonia, the yeasts actually took it into themselves as food.

He now devised a final demonstration to show that the yeasts grew rather than decreased during fermentation. In his fantastic solution he produced a kilogram of pure white yeast from an amount of yeast no bigger than the head of a pin.

This done, he invited Liebig to Paris to view all the work that had demolished the theory of fermentation by chemical action.

He sighed in triumph when Liebig refused the invitation. The battle was over.

He had won.

Actually, so far as the rest of the world of science was concerned, the fight was far from over. Some scientists applauded him; others scorned him. Liebig steadfastly refused to acknowledge the truth of his discovery. Years would pass before the Pasteur theory of living and specific ferments would be fully accepted.

But Louis was certain—absolutely certain—it would stand the test of time. And he was positive it would be of growing service to distillers over the world. He had been unable to help Monsieur Bigo cure his bad fermentations, but now he had given the little man at Lille and all his fellow alcohol producers the key to prevention of bad fermentations. The knowledge of what caused all fermentations would enable them to control the troublesome ones.

And so his mind began to turn to other questions. The little bugs that caused fermentations—all the millions of little bugs found everywhere—where did they come from? Did they have parents? How were they born? How many of them were in the air?

Such questions were to bring him to grips with the oldest scientific riddle of all.

The Oldest Riddle
of Them All

Louis' tone was furious. "What did you say?"

Marie glanced up from her knitting, then lowered her eyes again quickly. Her husband's newspaper had dropped to his lap and his thirty-seven-year-old face was dark with anger. She knew she had ruined a pleasant evening at home in 1859 for him. "I said that Professor Dumas paid me a visit this afternoon. He asked me to convince you to stop your spontaneous generation experiments."

Now the paper struck the floor as Louis bounded to his feet. He paced the length of the living room. "This is too much! Really too much! Ever since I began the experiments several months ago, all my friends have tried to talk me out of them—Balard, Dumas, even Biot. I haven't minded; they're entitled to their opinions. But now they are trying to turn my wife against me. That's going too far!"

"Professor Dumas said—"

"I know very well what he said. I've heard it all a hundred times before." His hands clasped and unclasped themselves behind his back in perfect rhythm with his sentences. "Spontaneous generation is a useless subject, important to no one! I'm involving myself in something that has no answer! I'm wasting time that could be spent on more valuable work!"

"Are you wasting your time, Louis?"

"Absolutely not! Spontaneous generation is a theory that my fermentation studies have led me to believe is false. It's not a waste of time to prove to science that it *is* false. We can't live in ignorance forever." He halted his pacing, regarded Marie closely. "Do *you* think I'm wasting my time?"

"I don't know enough about the subject to say."

"Then you shall learn—and right now." He hurried to the chair opposite her and sat down. "Very simply, it is a theory that states that living things can spring to life from nothing. Poof, like that!" He snapped his fingers, laughing. His rage had vanished as quickly as it had come. He was now the enthusiastic teacher, leading his pupil into the unknown.

"It's a belief that goes back to the beginning of recorded history," he said. "For instance, the ancients thought that frogs, eels, and fish came from the mud of rivers. Caterpillars were believed to spring from leaves. Even the great Virgil wasn't free from such thinking. He claimed that bees came into existence in the entrails of dead bulls.

"Such beliefs continued through the Middle Ages and the Renaissance. Van Helmont, a noted scientist of the sixteenth century, wrote that mice could be spontaneously generated— made to spring to life from nothing—by merely placing a few bits of cheese along with some dirty linen in a container."

Marie laughed outright. "Didn't he stop to think that the cheese might have attracted the mice from other parts of the house?"

"Apparently not. But we mustn't think him stupid. He lived in an age of little real scientific knowledge and equipment," Louis said. "Fortunately, the years produced scientists who questioned the authenticity of spontaneous generation. One such man was the Italian Francesco Redi."

Redi, Louis related, was physician to the Grand Duke of Tuscany. He had been told that maggots sprang to life in decaying meat. "That must not have sounded right to him, for he decided to see exactly what happened to a bit of decaying meat. It wasn't long before he noticed that blowflies were swarming about the stuff. He began to wonder if the flies were responsible for the maggots, and so he placed chunks of meat in jars covered with gauze. Though the meat decayed not one maggot appeared. But Redi saw the flies settle on the gauze and saw the maggots arise. Here at last was the answer. The maggots came from eggs laid on the gauze by the flies."

Louis' delight at the story caused Marie to dip her head ceremoniously and intone, "Bravo!"

"Bravo, indeed, for, because of men like Redi, people slowly got over the idea of spontaneous generation. They came to realize that creatures such as insects, frogs, fish, eels, and worms just don't spring to life from nothing, as if by a miracle. They got to know that these creatures must have parents. The theory of spontaneous generation seemed dead."

"Dead?" Marie's dark brows lifted. "Then why are you studying it today?"

"I'm coming to that," Louis said. "In the seventeenth century, Antony Leeuwenhoek developed the microscope and a vast new world came within our view, a world of millions of tiny beings. Thousands of them could be seen on a crumb of bread or in a drop of water. You can imagine the feelings of the poor scientists!" Louis flattened his palms against his temples and rocked his head to and fro. "Millions and millions of little bugs. Where did they come from? How were they born? No one knew. And so some scientists began to claim they sprang from nothing. The theory of spontaneous generation was born again. It lives to this day, causing argument on all sides. Many scientists call it sheer nonsense. But many more insist it is the truth."

Louis jumped to his feet and hurried from the room. A moment later, he reappeared, pulling a sheaf of papers, dog-eared and scarred with pencil marks, from a leather brief-case.

"Here is the latest attack in favor of spontaneous generation," he said disdainfully—"a report made to the Academy of Sciences by Professor F. A. Pouchet, Director of the Museum of Natural History at Rouen."

As Marie thumbed through the papers, Louis explained, "In recent years, a number of scientists who oppose spontaneous generation have attempted to show that germs are really the children of other germs that can be found floating in the air. But see what Pouchet says! He writes he saw germs spring to life in solutions he had placed in bottles from which all air had been removed. No germs could have been brought in from the outside, he says. Consequently, he claims spontaneous generation is true, and then—" Louis' finger jabbed the manuscript, "and then he claims his experiment also proves that *the air, the atmosphere, contains no living organisms at all!*"

This latter thought was too much for Louis. "No living organisms in the air! It's nonsense! The man's made a mistake somewhere. He's dead wrong. And I'm proving him wrong." He gripped Marie's hands. "Do you now see how important I feel this work in spontaneous generation to be? The truth about how all life begins—this is something the world must know. Knowledge must replace old superstitions if progress is to be made. Perhaps, as my friends say, there is no answer to spontaneous generation. Perhaps it is too big and too confusing to be answered. Perhaps I will find myself involved in a useless argument with men like Pouchet. But I don't think I should quit. And I don't think I'm wasting my time. Do you?"

Marie's reply lifted a great weight from his shoulders. "Of course I don't, Louis. Does anyone who searches for truth waste his time?"

The scientist leaned far back in his chair. "Thank you, my dear."

"You say you are proving Pouchet wrong. How?"

"By a very simple experiment involving some guncotton. So far, it's shown him completely wrong. But I'm repeating it daily to remove all chance of error. Tomorrow I shall try it again." He grinned at the ceiling in anticipation of the next day's work. "Young Duclaux will have all the necessary equipment ready first thing in the morning. He has been of more help than you can possibly imagine."

True to his prediction, Louis found all preparation for the

experiment completed upon his arrival at the lab. Émile
Duclaux stood by a work bench on which were neatly
arranged an aspirator, a wad of guncotton, and a bottle containing a solution of ether and alcohol.

Louis scanned the equipment approvingly. "Good. Good.
Where is my notebook?"

"I have it here, Professor."

Ah, the efficient Duclaux! He missed nothing, the slender,
dark-complexioned man of twenty-two. Not too long ago, he
had been one of Louis' finer students and now the university
had appointed him assistant to the scientist. The arrangement pleased Louis mightily. The boy was as meticulous in
his work as his features were sharp, and as brilliant as his
steep forehead suggested.

"Today we'll see if there are any germs floating about right
under our noses," Louis said. He carefully tamped the guncotton into the aspirator, a slender tube with a plunger at
one end and open at the other. "And, you may take my word
for it, there are."

Émile watched him hold the tube face high and begin to
work the plunger. This was a strange Pasteur this morning.
A Pasteur who hummed and chuckled to himself as he drew
a stream of air through the tube. Usually the scientist carried
out the simplest of experiments in an intense, almost angry
silence. But today he seemed as carefree as the most empty-
headed of students. Perhaps he had finally managed to dis-
miss from mind all the arguments of his friends who wanted
him to abandon his current study.

"The air passes through the tube, so." Louis seemed to be
speaking to himself. "The little germs bump into the cotton.
They can go no further. They become the prisoners of

young Monsieur Duclaux and the Pasteur who is accused of wasting his time. There! That's enough. The tweezers, please, Émile."

While Louis busied himself extracting the guncotton from the aspirator, Émile moved the bottle of solution to the scientist's elbow. The cotton, white a few moments ago, was now a dull gray. Into the bottle it went. Liquid closed over it, seeped into its every pore, dissolved it, and left only a gray residue at the bottom of the bottle.

Flecks of this darkish residue were transferred to a microscope stage. Louis' enjoyment of the morning reached its peak. Revealed to him was a world of churning activity in every fleck. There were tiny germs beyond count, all of them moving convulsively in the highly serious business of staying alive. There were germs of all shapes and sizes, germs that men never thought of when taking a breath.

Louis pulled Émile to the microscope. "We've found our proof again, just as we've found it every morning for weeks. So Pouchet says there are no living organisms in the air? Well, there they are—pulled out of the atmosphere and shattering his claim with their every movement. And look! Do you see the little spores, the eggs of germs about to be born? *They're proof that these microscopic creatures are born of parents instead of springing into being from nothing!*"

Once again the scientist took his place at the instrument. He heard Émile say, "Professor, we've performed this experiment more times than I can count. Shouldn't we make our findings known?"

"Not yet," Louis said. "Pouchet will say one kind of experiment isn't enough. And he will be right. We need more proof. We need another type of experiment that will back up what we've found here."

That second experiment had to wait until Louis had lived through a personal tragedy. It was a tragedy that blackened his life for weeks to come. A pale Marie, her face stiff with the effort of holding back tears, brought him the news that little Jeanne, who had been vacationing with her grandfather at Arbois, had suddenly contracted typhoid fever. The little girl of the dark, tossing braids and the inquisitive mind was dead.

Silently, trying to pass whatever strength they had from one to the other through their clasped hands, Louis and Marie travelled by train to Arbois and saw their oldest child buried alongside her grandmother. Louis felt a cold anger steal through his grief as he stood in the cemetery. It was an anger he directed at himself. He had spent a life-time toying with crystals and peering at tiny germs and wondering from whence they came. What a wasted life it suddenly seemed to be! He should have spent his time attacking this vicious thing called disease, this blind thing that struck out at all human beings, even the smallest of children. He heard himself whisper a promise to Jeanne. Somehow, someday, he would fight this evil thing. He'd fight it wherever he found it. And he'd smash it.

Louis and Marie lingered in Arbois for several days, reluctant to leave the place where their daughter had spent her last hours. They received old friends and heard words of comfort that could not comfort them. Then, realizing they must begin to piece their broken lives together again, they paid Jeanne's grave a last visit and started back to Paris.

Marie had to get back to Cécile and to Marie-Louise, who was now almost a year old, and Jean-Baptiste had to return to school. And Louise had his work.

For months to come, the scientist had no taste for that work or its rewards. The Prize for Experimental Physiology, awarded him by the Academy of Sciences in January, 1860, for his fermentation studies, meant nothing to him. And he wondered how he had ever thought spontaneous generation fascinating.

But, little by little, the hard clot of grief in his chest dissolved. The memories of Jeanne and her laughter remained as sharp as ever, but the pain they brought was gradually dulling. Life was beginning anew. The spring of 1860 found him again searching for the experiment that would prove once and for all that microscopic life existed in the atmosphere.

It was Antoine Balard who provided the idea Louis needed. The aging chemist bounded into the lab one morning to ask about the current work of his one-time assistant and learned that the desired second experiment had not yet come to mind.

Pudgy fingers drummed the work bench. Balard's face became a thoughtful moon. "So you need more proof, eh? Louis, you are now a master, but perhaps you will consent to become a student again long enough to hear a little idea of mine."

"Of course, Professor."

"Good."

Balard's ample frame settled itself on a work stool. He drew Louis' notebook to himself. His voice was full of delight. "I am not an artist, what? But you will recognize this to be a flask," he said as he drew:

"Now in this flask we place some yeast solution, purified of all little germs by boiling. Then we heat the neck of the flask and draw the glass out into a long, curved tube. Like so. . . ."

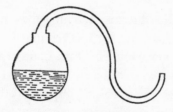

"And," he concluded, "we leave the end of the tube open."

Louis slapped his forehead. "Of course! I see what you're getting at. It's so simple. Why didn't I think of it?"

Balard cocked a fuzzy eyebrow and winked. "Sometimes brilliant men forget the little, the simple things. I know. I'm always doing it myself. And I'm very bright." He tapped his crude sketch. "Now you allow air to enter the tube. You'll find that the solution remains pure. The little germs in the atmosphere will never reach it. They'll become trapped in the lower part of the curve because the dust that carries them won't be able to work its way upwards."

Already Louis' mind was at work on how he would use this masterpiece of simplicity. "Then to show that germs really travel in the air, I'll do two things. First, I'll sever the tube at the neck of the flask. New air will rush into the container and I'll see little creatures growing in the solution that, until then, had remained pure."

"Correct. It will also show that the solution did not cause germs to generate spontaneously. Micro-organisms had to enter from the air before life appeared."

"Then I'll take the second, and truly important, step," Louis said. "I'll wash a purified solution through the curved tube. If germs are really trapped in the curve, they'll be picked up by the solution and I'll be able to see them easily."

"Exactly."

Duclaux, from a distance watching the eminent scientists gaze enrapt at the drawing, was reminded of two children mesmerized by a new toy. He heard Louis say, "It's beautiful —as graceful as the neck of a swan."

Balard nodded. He gazed happily round the room. "Two different kinds of experiment to substantiate your belief. Louis, that should be quite enough proof for anyone, even the stubborn Professor F. A. Pouchet!"

CHAPTER 8

Mountains to Climb

But the experiments did not provide enough proof. Not for Pouchet. And not for the two scientists who had recently joined forces with him, Nicholas Joly and Charles Musset.

"Professor Pasteur claims his pretty experiments illustrate that infant germs must be born of other germs floating in the air," they chorused. "We find it impossible to believe that the atmosphere is packed with tiny bugs, all giving birth to other tiny bugs. Why, if that were so, every ounce of air would be dense as iron with them. They would make it impossible for people to breathe."

The three men then advanced a theory of their own. "His experiments actually prove the truth of spontaneous generation. What happened in his laboratory is this: *the oxygen in the air which entered his test tubes caused new life to generate spontaneously!* The little germs had nothing to do with it."

The arguments infuriated Louis. The three men were maddening. They seemed willing to use any excuse to deny the importance of microscopic life and to substantiate their belief in spontaneous generation. Oxygen caused new life! Bah! He'd have to prove them wrong. But how?

He found the answer in his notes on the recent experiments and immediately ordered Duclaux to fill twenty-one flasks with a solution of yeast extract, sugar, and water. Then he himself drew the neck of each flask out to a tiny opening over the flame of an alcohol lamp. Next the solutions were boiled to kill any impurities and to drive out the air, and, while the boiling was taking place, each flask was sealed by melting the tip of its glass neck with a blowpipe. Louis surveyed the results with satisfaction; the vessels were almost completely devoid of air and the solutions would remain pure until the glass necks were broken. He grinned at Duclaux.

"You're wondering what the purpose of all this is, I suppose?" He picked up his notebook. "I found the clue to answer Pouchet and his friends right here. You recall how we discovered that the germs in our solutions varied, depending on where we took our samples of atmosphere. Sometimes the number was great, sometimes small. Well, it has occurred to me that perhaps the air is thick with germs in some places and relatively free of them in others. . . ."

Duclaux began to nod enthusiastically. From the sudden glitter in Émile's eyes, Louis knew the boy had already guessed his plan.

"So," he continued, "we will take our flasks to both places. Many germs should appear in flasks opened in dusty areas where microscopic life is plentiful. And few, if any, in the vessels opened in pure air. If this happens, Pouchet will have to admit that only germs can produce other germs. They will have produced life according to their numbers in the air. Pouchet will have no further reason for saying oxygen creates new life."

Ten of the flasks were carried to the cellar of the Observatory of Paris. Here the air was calm, cool, and undisturbed. Quickly, Louis and Émile set to the work they had rehearsed so carefully in the lab. Émile sterilized long-nosed pincers with an alcohol lamp. Louis held each flask, one after the other, high above his head, for he wished not one particle of dust from his clothing to enter the vessels, and snipped the glass necks with the pincers. There was a hissing sound of inrushing air, after which each flask was resealed.

The two men hurried the flasks into incubators back at the lab and then returned to the Observatory with the remaining eleven of the twenty-one flasks they had prepared, this time setting their equipment down in the front yard. The traffic of Paris trundled past on all sides as they opened and then resealed the flasks. There were fine carriages and cabs, refuse carts, and goods wagons. There were men, women, and children, some of whom paused to stare at the scientists and their little bottles. There was even a dog who ventured up close and sniffed curiously at Louis' heels. And there were germs. You couldn't see them, Louis told himself, but they were there—rising from the litter at the curbs, swirling off the carts, even bounding out of the feathers atop those fashionable but ridiculous hats worn by the passing ladies. Yes, they were there, Louis thought contentedly, and they had to be pouring into his flasks by the thousands.

Back in the lab, scientist and assistant arranged the twenty-one flasks on a work bench. Louis passed from one to the other restlessly, like a finicky general hoping to find some soldier's buttons unpolished. At each, he crouched low and peered at the solution within. His face was flushed and he kept readjusting his spectacles on the wide bridge of his nose. It wasn't long before he began mumbling to himself, and then he was directing his words to an Émile whose excitement matched his own.

"We've done it! Look at them! Ah, those lovely flasks. They're going to redden the faces of Pouchet, Joly and Musset. The solutions in all eleven opened in the dirty air of the yard are now teeming with new life. But only one of the ten opened in the calm, almost dust-free air of the cellar has shown any change. The solutions in the other nine remain pure. This should remove all doubt. Only germs can give birth to other germs. If oxygen produced life, all the solutions should now be crowded with almost equal numbers of germs!"

This simple experiment captured the public's fancy. Spontaneous generation became a topic for discussion in hotels, restaurants, shops; it even divided some families at their firesides. Pouchet, Joly, Musset and their supporters continued to scoff at Louis, and the editor of the *Moniteur Scientifique* grandly wrote, "What will be the outcome of this giant's struggle?" Happily, Louis noted, the Academy of Sciences was on his side. And, best of all, he learned that Biot and Dumas had recognized the value of his work. Both men now urged him to continue his battle to disprove spontaneous generation. Once again their attitude seemed to say, "Pasteur is defeating the impossible."

In the summer of 1860, Louis closed his ears to the public clamor and readied himself for an experiment that would

take him high into the Swiss Alps. The experiment at the
Observatory hadn't been enough for him. He now wanted
to obtain data concerning the amounts of microscopic beings
at varying altitudes. He set Émile to the task of filling with
yeast extract solution and then sealing more than one hundred flasks.

The first leg of his journey took him to a country road
outside Arbois. Arbois! How full of memories of his mother
and little Jeanne it was.

He must not think of the memories, he told himself, and
he must not think of the farmers who passed by and wondered what a full-grown man was doing down on his knees
in the dust with all those strange little bottles. He had work
to do—the work of opening twenty flasks, of hearing the
now familiar sounds of inrushing air, of resealing the glass
necks and waiting impatiently for the liquids to cloud with
life that the naked eye could not see. It was work that
climaxed with the scribbled words in his notebook: "The
solutions in only eight out of the twenty vessels tested showed
signs of change. The air of Arbois is purer than that of
Paris."

His next stop was Mount Poupet in Switzerland. After a
sleepless night of wondering if the sway and rattle of the
train had broken any of the phials, he opened another twenty
of them at a height of one hundred and fifty meters above
sea level. He felt a sharp pain in his chest from all the climb-
ing and realized he was getting a bit too old for this type of
adventuring. But he didn't care, for now only five bottles
revealed new life. He added another fact to his knowledge—
the higher the altitude, the cleaner the air.

On September 20, 1860, Louis arrived in the Swiss town of

Chamonix at the base of the Montanvert. He rented a donkey and hired a guide to lead him up the icy face of the mountain. The guide massaged a leathery, underslung jaw and shrugged. This Frenchman is quite mad, wanting to put all those bottles on a donkey's back and drag them up a narrow, dangerous trail for the pleasure of opening and then closing them again. "But he has good money, so why should I complain. He's a scientist and a Frenchman. He can't be anything but mad!"

The following morning, the guide found another reason for thinking his client demented. Louis insisted on walking abreast of the donkey to steady the thirty-two flasks strapped in cases to the animal's back. His feet were but scant inches from the edge of the trail. If the wind knocked him off-balance or the donkey bumped against him—

The guide shrugged.

It was a long fall.

The climb lasted several hours and only Louis' determination to see the experiment completed kept him from turning back. His every muscle soon cried out against the steepness of the ascent. The wind drove his scarf straight out behind him, numbed his hands, set his face afire and drove an icy knife deep into his lungs. Ice crystals, swirling off the white slopes, frosted his eyebrows, lashes, and beard. The thinning air dizzied him, turned each breath into a tortured gasp.

He survived all this discomfort only to face disappointment when, crouching in the snow, he opened the first of his flasks.

He had brought along a spirit lamp with which to seal the flasks. Now as he held it close to the severed neck of the first phial, he found that the thin jet of flame was almost invisible against the whiteness of the ground. Too, the wind toyed with the flame, flicking it back and forth, never allowing it to spray the glass with its heat long enough to seal the flask properly.

The guide, who did not understand the purpose of his experiment but recognized his difficulty, suggested, "Why don't you put the bottle inside one of the cases to shield it from the wind?"

"No! No! No!" Louis shouted testily. "Dust from the case would enter the solution. That mustn't happen."

The guide shrugged. His great moustache dropped with the falling corners of his mouth. He said petulantly, "I was only trying to help."

Instantly, Louis regretted his words. "I'm not angry with you," he apologized. "It's just that I'm disappointed. I've come such a long way to have this happen." He struggled to his feet. "There is no use going on with this today. We'll try again tomorrow."

The guide ran pale blue eyes over the length of his client. The Frenchman was a sight with ice spray covering him from head to foot, face a mottled red, lips blue, and teeth wanting to chatter. Try again tomorrow? Why, the man would never make it.

But Louis did make it, and managed to reach an even higher elevation. Once again he crouched in the snow with his flasks arranged in front of him like an irregular line of midget soldiers. Last night he had sent the guide to a smithy to have the lamp altered so that it gave a wider, larger flame. All that could be done had been done. Either the lamp would do its job or it wouldn't. No shield could be used lest such a device release germs into the solutions.

Louis worked quickly. As he took up each flask, he circled the neck with a thin line made with a steel cutting tool. He was careful not to cut too deeply. Not a single iota of dust from the tool must find its way into the solution. Now the flask went above his head, away from the germs of his own breath. Long-nosed pincers snapped off the neck at the thin line. He lowered the bottle and aimed the spirit lamp at it. The flame, its blue and orange stream now visible against the snow, stabbed the glass, melted it, and sealed the neck. Louis settled back into a crouch. The effort had left him trembling and gasping. But he was satisfied. It had been a job well done.

Twenty times he repeated the process before leaving the mountain. In a tiny inn at the base of the Montanvert, while sheep grazed lazily on distant knolls that looked so near in the thin air, Louis watched the end of the experiment that was to astound the scientific world. In that small room, with its oversized bed and worn carpet, only one of the twenty flasks showed evidence of new life.

Louis rocked back and forth on the edge of the giant bed, his hands gripping his knees. He was exhausted, but triumphant. It was now a certainty. He had disproven the ancient theory of spontaneous generation once and for all. There could be no doubt that his findings on the distribution of germs in the atmosphere demonstrated conclusively that all microscopic life depended entirely on other microscopic life for its birth.

In his notebook he wrote: "If all the results are compared that I have obtained until now, it seems to me that it can be affirmed that the dusts suspended in natural air are the exclusive origin and the necessary condition of life in the liquids in the vessels."

He looked at what he had written and wondered how Pouchet, Joly, and Musset would react to this.

That reaction was not heard until late in 1863. In the meantime, Louis returned to his classes and his studies on fermentation, completing late in the year the paper, *Mémoire sur la fermentation alcoolique,* which established once and for all that living organisms cause fermentations and that a specific kind of germ is required for each. He delivered two lectures before the Société Chimique de Paris and earned from the Academy of Sciences the Jecker Prize for his fermentation studies and the Alhumbert Prize for his work in spontaneous generation. In his laboratory he discovered that certain forms of germ life can exist without air. He classified these germs as "anaerobic life."

The crowning events of these years were his election to the Academy of Sciences in the section of mineralogy on December 8, 1862, and the birth of Camile, his fifth and last child, in 1863. Both occurrences filled him with pride and the former erased the keen disappointment he had felt over his failure to gain entry to the Academy just six years before.

His election was marred by sadness, for the man who had done so much to encourage his scientific genius could not be there to see him seated. Earlier in the year, Marie had come to the laboratory to tell him quietly of the news being circulated by the newspapers—that death had finally ended the long career of Jean Baptiste Biot.

Louis' grief was dry-eyed. After all, Biot had lived a long and useful life. Death was to be expected. But that did nothing to ease Louis' sense of loss. Though the elderly scientist had sometimes strained Louis' nerves and though their paths had crossed with less frequency these past years, the spirit of Biot had always seemed to stand at the younger man's shoulder, encouraging him, driving him on to greater effort. "But perhaps it matters not that he is gone," Louis thought. "Surely the spirit will remain."

In the autumn of 1863, the reaction of Pouchet, Joly, and Musset to his traveling experiment reached Louis, first from the newspapers and then from a written report by the men themselves.

"Look how they tried to outdo me," he told Émile Duclaux. "They took flasks containing solutions of hay to the Rencluse in Switzerland. It's a much higher peak than the Montanvert. They completed their first tests and then decided to go even higher." After spending the night on the windswept mountain they had struggled up to the foot of the Maladetta glaciers. Louis chuckled, remembering his own discomfort in the snow. They must have been frozen through and through. But he could not help but admire their courage. "They opened four flasks on the Maladetta, sealed them, and brought them back to Luchon. Poor Musset! He was almost killed in a fall on the trip down."

Now the scientist's face clouded with bewilderment. "They found that the liquids in *all* the flasks had changed. All revealed the presence of microscopic life!" He cast the paper aside suddenly, angrily, and began to march up and down the lab. "So we are right back in the middle of the fight again! They claim that I was incorrect in my observations, that I made some error in my experiment. They say their findings definitely prove that microscopic life can be spontaneously generated from the oxygen in the atmosphere!"

"And you say?"

"I say, as always, that spontaneous generation is impossible. And I say these men are wrong. They, not I, have made a mistake somewhere. And that is exactly what I'm going to tell the world!"

For weeks, French newspapers crowded their pages with the debate. Each side searched for new proofs and restated old ones. Neither camp gave an inch to the other. Louis' fraying patience was saved from complete ruin by the knowledge that the Academy of Sciences had sided with him. Finally, in November, Pouchet and his two followers suggested the Academy appoint a commission to hear both sides of the argument and render a verdict that would settle it forever, saying, "If a single one of our flasks remains unaltered, we shall loyally acknowledge our defeat." Louis agreed to the idea, and Marie Jean Flourens, Alexandre Brongniart, Milne-Edwards, Dumas, and the volatile Balard were appointed to the Commission. The trial was set for March, 1864.

Louis and Duclaux immediately began to prepare the sixty flasks they planned to put before the Commission. However, the beginning of 1864 brought the news that Pouchet had requested the trial be postponed until summer.

"It seems he thinks the cool weather of March will somehow affect the results of his experiment," Émile explained.

The reasoning bewildered Louis, but he cocked an eyebrow and winked. "Perhaps Pouchet and his friends are no longer so sure of themselves. Ah, well, I agree to wait until summer."

But the first month of summer brought another request for postponement from Pouchet. The Commission granted it, only to learn next that the man from Rouen and his followers were withdrawing from the trial altogether.

Louis threw back his head in laughter. "They suggested the trial and now they are running from it. Perhaps they have discovered they made some sort of error up on the Maladetta." His eyes were glittering pinpoints behind thick glasses. "Well, we shall not run. The Commission will hear *us*."

Accordingly, he faced that body of distinguished scientists in the laboratory of Michel Chevreul at the Museum of Natural History. The assistants who followed him into the room were laden with flasks, pincers, alcohol lamps, and cutting tools. Balard grinned and nudged Dumas. "The meek student is now the lion," he joked quietly. "He fights even when there is no one to fight!"

Balard grew serious, however, when the members of the Commission got down to the business of watching Louis present the first of his proofs. He showed them three flasks he had sealed on the Montanvert in 1861 and had not opened since. He now snipped the neck of one. Its air and solution were analyzed; the air contained a normal amount of oxygen and the solution, *after three years*, was free of microscopic life. Three days later, much to Louis' delight, the bottle was swimming with germs.

He now moved his demonstration to the amphitheater of the Museum. He opened nineteen of the sixty flasks he had prepared and the Commission saw that only five of them became clouded with new life. Next he led the panting scientists up narrow stairs to the highest part of the dome of the amphitheater and opened another nineteen flasks; the little germs failed to appear in all but six of them. Finally, the five weary members had to follow this seemingly tireless Pasteur out into the open air and watch him open eighteen flasks beneath a poplar tree close to passing traffic, and they had to return his triumphant smile when microscopic life appeared in all but *two* of the vessels.

"There you are, gentlemen!" His voice held the ring of victory. "All the proof you need. The first vessels I demonstrated had been boiled to purify them long before I used them on the Montanvert; old germs had been killed and no new ones had appeared in three whole years; no spontaneous generation occurred. Very few germs appeared in the flasks opened in the relatively clean air of the amphitheater and its dome. But thousands upon thousands of new bugs showed themselves in the vessels broken open in the dirty outside air." He searched each face intently. "Can you now say that germs are not born of other germs? Can you now say spontaneous generation is true?"

They couldn't, and several weeks later their verdict was published in the *Comptes Rendus* of the Academy of Sciences. Pasteur was the winner. The fight was over. Microorganisms depended entirely on other micro-organisms for life. The theory of spontaneous generation was false.

Science's oldest riddle was solved.

CHAPTER

9

The Scientific Juggler

Between 1864 and 1868, Louis came to see himself as a juggler of scientific riddles.

His "juggling" began when Emperor Napoleon III, who had followed his career with admiration, asked him to investigate a strange disease that was destroying the excellent flavor of French wines and costing the nation's wine industry millions of francs annually.

It was a great honor to be thus singled out by the Emperor, and Louis hurried to the task. A preliminary study of the disease prompted him to tell Émile Duclaux, "I suspect it's nothing more than an assortment of fermentations. Look at the effect it has on the wines of different areas. Some become acid. Some become turbid, release gas, and acquire a flat taste. Others become ropy and still others bitter. Such facts can mean but one thing: each wine is being attacked by a specific kind of germ and is being fermented—or changed —into another substance."

His first task was to collect the various sick wines and track down their little germs. The villainous micro-organisms could not hide themselves long from his searching eye, and, early in 1865, he showed Émile drawings he had made of several different types.

"First, here are the fellows who swim about in the wines gone bitter," he exclaimed. "Have you ever seen things that resembled infinitesimal strings of spaghetti more than they? And here are the ones in the acid-tasting wines. What do they look like?"

"Peanuts, I should think," Émile said after a moment's hesitation.

"You're right. Now see the ones in the ropy wines. You might easily mistake them for grains of sand." Louis tossed the drawings aside. "It's exactly as I thought. The disease is a collection of fermentations, each one caused by a different bug. Now our problem is to rid each wine of its kind of bug. . . ."

His voice faded. He stared at the drawings thoughtfully. Émile laughed and picked up his thought.

"But how?"

Louis glanced at the boy out of the corners of his eyes. He smiled slowly. "Yes. How? That's the question of the year."

He had no time to go in quest of the answer, for Professor Dumas, at the urging of the Minister of Agriculture, entered the lab the next day and urged him to take on a second problem. The scientific juggling was beginning in earnest.

"But, Professor," a flabbergasted Louis stammered, "I know absolutely nothing of silkworms."

"I am well aware of that," Dumas replied. Hair iron gray and thick features seamed by time, he sat erect and well tailored on a wooden chair, his attitude so grave as to be slightly pompous. But Louis could not condemn that attitude. Dumas' problem was serious, alarmingly serious. "And so is the Minister of Agriculture."

"Then how can he hope that I'll be able to wipe out this disease of the silkworms, this—" Louis gestured helplessly— "what do you call it again?"

"Pébrine."

"See? I don't even know its name. I wouldn't know where to begin to fight it."

Dumas shrugged impatiently. That point was of no real consequence. "You will find out where to begin. Like everyone in this country, the Minister considers you a laboratory magician. That is why he has sent me to ask you to rid the silk industry of this malady."

Louis opened his mouth, but had no chance to speak before Dumas threw his bulk forward and jabbed the scientist's knee. "And pébrine *must* be destroyed. Do you realize the business of raising silkworms is one of this nation's greatest industries? Do you realize its income amounts to one hundred thousand francs a year?"

"Of course. Every schoolboy knows that. So many people earn their living from the industry that, if I remember correctly, they call the mulberry tree on which the silkworm feeds the Tree of Gold."

"That's right. And unless this disease, pébrine, is quickly halted there will be no more silkworm industry in France. Thousands will be jobless. Starving. The economy of the entire country will suffer." The picture of doom he painted set Dumas to wheezing noisily.

"Still," Louis insisted, "I think the Minister has picked

the wrong man. He should find a person experienced in silkworm cultivation. Would you give me a little time to think
this over?"

"Certainly." Dumas sighed and stood, disappointed he had
not immediately won Louis' support. He mustered a final
shot. "You have never shirked your duty before. I don't
expect you to shirk it now."

The next day Louis gave to a study of the raising of silkworms. He learned of things he had never known before—
that moths laid eggs from which the silkworms were
hatched, that the worms were fed mulberry leaves until,
after shedding their hides four times, they encased themselves in cocoons of a threadlike material that came from
glands in their heads. He learned that each cocoon was
dipped in hot water to kill the worm before it turned into a
moth and ruined the cocoon by breaking out of it. The
threadlike material of the cocoon was then unwound and
spun into silk.

Next he turned to a paper written by his friend, Quatre-
fages. It traced the silk industry from its legendary beginnings in China four thousand years ago to the point in 1845
when it was a worldwide enterprise. In that year, the first
symptoms of a strange disease were noticed. The next years
witnessed the spread of the disease over the world. France,
Italy, Spain, Austria, Turkey, and even China were attacked.
Today, in 1865, only Japan remained free of the curse.

The world had given the disease many names. Italian silkworm cultivators called it "gattine," from *gattino,* meaning
kitten, because sick worms thrust up their heads and extended their hooked feet like cats about to scratch. In
France, the name "pébrine" had been adopted. It came from

the word for pepper, *pébre;* infected worms always revealed brown and black spots resembling pepper grains..

"What a maddening thing it is," Louis told Marie. "It strikes its victims in all stages of their development—as an egg, a worm, a chrysalis, and a moth. Sometimes it appears suddenly, sometimes it develops over a long period. Sometimes it disappears for a while, only to break out again later."

By the time he had finished his study, Louis' imagination was afire. Someone had to help the thousands of people of all nationalities in this industry, even if that someone had never once touched a silkworm in all his life. If a cure was found, it would circle the globe. It would find its way to hillsides and valleys and villages he had never heard of and would never see. It would restore prosperity to the lives of a number he could never begin to count. His vision staggered him and left him with but one answer for Dumas. He wrote his former teacher, "Do as you like with me."

The attack on pébrine was launched in June of 1865. Louis and three assistants carried their microscopes south to Alais, the heart of the French silkworm industry, and established a makeshift laboratory that, though they could not know it at the time, was to be a place of hardship and disappointment for them every silkworm season for four years to come.

They encountered the first of those hardships at their initial meeting with the cultivators of the area. They were a stolid, proud lot, these cultivators, with their dark berets angling down over their foreheads and the ends of soiled neckerchiefs tucked inside woolen shirt fronts. Their faces were squarish, their brows dark, their skins leathery from years in the outdoors. They were slow of movement, soft of speech, but their eyes were hostile. Louis guessed the reason for their hostility immediately.

"Can you tell me," he asked, "what you have done to fight pébrine thus far?"

The answers were so startling that he might have laughed had it not been for the smouldering eyes and sullen voices.

"I dust the worms with ashes, charcoal, and sulfur," one cultivator said.

"That's a waste of time," another said.

"Don't say I waste my time!"

"All right, Pierre, you don't waste your time. But you should use chlorine gas or coal tar. Then you might become rich and stingy again."

There was a moment of hard, humorless laughter. It was born of desperation. Then a voice spoke from the back of the group: "You should use my method—sprinkle the mulberry leaves with wine and rum."

More hard laughter. "Rum!" That's for pirates, André. What do you want your worms to do? Sail away to the Spanish Main?"

"Better they should sail away," André snapped, his swarthy face crimson, "than die!"

"Have any of these measures ever met with success?" Louis broke in.

Shrugs greeted the question. The men shifted from foot to foot. "No, Monsieur. But we had to do something. We could think of nothing else. Our industry was dying."

Then, from Louis' right, came the blunt explanation for the hostile eyes and sullen voices. "And it will go right on dying. What's the use of all this talk? We appealed to the Minister of Agriculture for help and who does he send us—a man who knows nothing of silkworms. What good will he do us?"

The group stirred nervously. The berets looked like a small, tossing sea. Louis heard rumblings of agreement and, here and there, a protest.

"But Professor Pasteur is a fine chemist. The papers say so."

"What do the papers know?" That was André.

"Give the man a chance." Pierre said.

"We don't have time to give him a chance," a man at the front of the group cried. "We're facing ruin at this very minute."

Having anticipated their hostility from the very first, Louis was ready for it. His mouth thinned and his jaw hardened. "Your industry is dying, yes, but it can recover if we work together. Perhaps I can find a cure. Perhaps not. At least I can try. Whether you trust my ability or not, I *am* the one the Minister has sent. Turn your backs on me and your industry is surely ruined. Help me and there is still a chance to save it."

The heated words, so unexpected from such a meek looking fellow, shocked the cultivators to silence. He wasn't one of their breed, but he had backbone just the same. "What sort of help do you want?" the man called André asked.

Louis was ready for this, too. He snatched his notebook from a work table and flipped it open. "Look at this," he said. The men closed in about him, wrinkling their brows at the little circles filled with dots that they found sketched on the open page. "Do you know what these drawings represent?"

One cultivator scratched his chin thoughtfully. "They look like what we call 'corpuscles.'"

"That's right. You've seen them before?"

"Certainly." The cultivator couldn't—or wouldn't—hide the sarcasm in his voice. "Anyone with an ounce of experience in this business has seen them. We often find them in our sick worms. It's very curious."

"It's more than just curious, my friend," Louis said. "I've learned that scientists investigating the disease suspect *that these tiny creatures actually cause pébrine*. I want to look into their theory." His gaze traveled from face to face. "I want you to bring me both healthy and unhealthy worms. I'll study them in my microscope. If the unhealthy ones all reveal the corpuscles and the healthy ones do not, we'll have reason to believe we've found the things responsible for the illness. Then we'll have to work to get rid of them."

"All right, Monsieur," André said. "We'll do as you ask."

The cultivators kept their word. They filled the makeshift lab to overflowing with trays of silkworms. Louis' days were spent at his microscope. He held great hope that he had sighted the cause of pébrine right off. The corpuscles were not present in the healthy worms. But they were easily observed in the sick ones; and their number increased until, at death, the poor animals were swarming with them.

His next step was to learn if the disease was contagious. He placed infected worms on mulberry leaves, removed them, and fed the leaves to healthy worms who fell sick immediately. He allowed others to be scratched, so very slightly, by diseased fellows. Illness followed swiftly. The final proof that pébrine was highly contagious was the fact that the larvae of eggs containing the corpuscles were likewise riddled with them.

Just as he started to work out a method for preventing the spread of the contagion, frightening news reached him from Arbois. His father was desperately ill. Louis' mind held but one thought as he dashed to the village—his mother and daughter had died before he could reach them. The same thing mustn't happen again. As soon as he descended to the station platform at the end of his journey, he knew he had lost his race with time. The relatives who had gathered to meet him were dressed in black.

Joseph Pasteur, the simple tanner and former soldier of Napoleon, was laid to rest beside his wife and granddaughter. Louis remained in Arbois for several weeks, attending to family affairs. Then back to Alais he went to throw himself completely into his work. It was the only way he knew to ease the pain his father's passing and the fresh sight of little Jeanne's grave had induced. Towards the end of summer he completed his plan for preventing the spread of pébrine. He summoned the cultivators to his lab and faced them confidently. He was certain his plan would melt their distrust of him.

"I'm certain that the corpuscles cause the disease, and my studies have shown me that pébrine is highly contagious," he told them. "The whole idea of my plan is to obtain a healthy crop of worms right at the very beginning of their lives, while they are yet eggs. We will simply separate the good eggs from the diseased ones as soon as they are laid and, in this way, halt pébrine before it has a chance to spread."

"How can this be done?" a cultivator asked.

"Very simply. After the eggs have been laid, open up the

bodies of both parents. If you find corpuscles in either or both of them, get rid of the eggs, for they, too, will have corpuscles. If you find no corpuscles in the parents, preserve the eggs and cultivate them carefully. Healthy worms will be hatched from them."

He surveyed the half-circle of squarish faces. In some of them he saw expressions of approval. Good. But, in others, there was undisguised doubt.

"This is going to be very expensive," a cultivator at the center of the group said. "It will mean throwing away hundreds of francs worth of eggs."

"It will be less costly than allowing pébrine to spread to *all* your eggs," Louis said gently. The objection was stupid but understandable. The cultivator had suffered such a financial loss that he couldn't think properly. Money was all that he had in mind. "And the sick eggs are useless anyway."

"Are you sure this is the best way?" asked a voice off to his left.

"Yes. In fact, it's the *only* method we can use until I can wipe the disease out altogether."

"But—"

André interrupted, impatiently. "Oh, stop arguing with the Professor. He may not raise silkworms himself, but his plan is worth trying. What can we lose?"

Louis sighed with relief as murmurs of assent dotted the crowd. Thank heavens for men like André! He knew he had won a goodly number of the cultivators to his side and he said, "Oh, I'm going to become a silkworm cultivator myself in just a few days, when I return to Paris for the beginning of school at the École Normale. I shall grow my own set of healthy worms so that I may continue studying pébrine until next year's silkworm season."

And so back to Paris he went at the end of the week with his assistants and his equipment. Back to Paris he went to await eagerly news of what success his method for preventing the spread of pébrine realized. And back to Paris he went to include in his scientific juggling again the problem of curing the sick wines.

"How can the wines be protected from their illness," he asked himself all the way home, "without ruining their flavor? I must look into this right away."

But, in a few days, he was to ask himself still another question, a question filled with burning tears.

"Why is it that every time I ready myself for new work tragedy fills my life?"

CHAPTER

10

Success, Failure, Success

Louis felt certain upon his arrival home that his two-year-old daughter, Camille, was the healthiest and happiest child in all Paris. She greeted him with shining eyes and proudly displayed the fact she had learned to speak in sentences during his long absence. She hurried her newest toys to him and they laughed at the ridiculous face of a rag doll. It was wonderful to see the child again, wonderful to see her in such perfect health, her cheeks glowing, her arms and legs so sturdy. Louis did not know a dread thing lurked nearby and that it would soon fill his life with grief.

That dread thing was typhoid fever. It gripped Camille in mid-September and choked Louis' heart with an icy fear. Was he going to lose another of his children? Death had stalked his family so often these past years. It must not now touch this tiny one. But he and all the fine medical doctors were powerless to ward off that touch. The doctors were able only to make the child comfortable, and Louis could do no more than hold her hand through each long night and hope and pray for her recovery.

The hope and prayers were in vain. Camille closed her eyes forever in late September. Rage, sorrow, despair—all these things welled up in Louis as he stared down at her quiet figure. Men called him famous. Men called his researches brilliant. Well, all the fame and all the researches were worthless, for they had not given him the ability to save the life of one tiny, fragile child. For a moment, it seemed to him as if he stood again at the grave of Jeanne. The very same words he had spoken there now rang with silent fury in his ears.

"Fight disease in humans. Fight it and kill it. That's what I must do—for Jeanne and now for you, my little Camille."

The promise was to be repeated a third time in his life, for the following spring—May of 1866—typhoid fever again visited the Pasteur home, spreading its terror and taking from Louis and Marie their twelve-year-old daughter, Cécile.

Work: it was the only thing that could blot out his sorrow. Louis filled his days with a hundred tasks, exhausted himself so that he could not help but sleep at night. He wrote an introduction to a book about Antoine Lavoisier, a scientist he much admired. He followed it with a paper of his own on the works of Claude Bernard. He battled a cholera epidemic in Paris. Nothing was learned from the fight. The disease passed on before a single new fact about it could be captured.

And he returned to the problem that had bothered him on the train up from Alais. How could wines be kept from going bad without spoiling their flavor? He experimented with a number of antiseptics. None worked. The taste of the treated wines was such that Émile Duclaux observed wryly, "The ones that have gone bad on their own are more palatable than these."

Then, quite suddenly one morning, a very simple remedy fell into mind.

"Heat them!" The words literally burst from Louis' mouth.

A startled Duclaux glanced up from a nearby work table. "Heat what?"

"Heat the wines." Louis was thoughtful, his fingers plucking at the corner of an eyebrow. "Yes. There's acid in the wines. Heating is a most effective disinfectant for acids. It should work nicely."

Émile shook his head. "I doubt it," he said at length, and then added two very vital questions: "Like everything else we've tried, won't it spoil their taste? And to what temperature must they be heated without ruining them?"

Patience and experimentation answered both questions. Louis soon found that when wines were heated to the temperature of fifty-five degrees centigrade the germs within were destroyed before they had a chance to do any damage.

"And the best part of the whole business," he chortled, "is that the flavor and aroma are not harmed one bit. The problem is solved—simply but effectively."

However, another problem loomed on the horizon. The public reacted to his process in exactly the same manner as had Émile.

Frenchmen everywhere threw up their hands in horror.

"Heat wines? But it is nonsense! The taste. The flavor. They cannot help but be ruined. No, no, Monsieur Pasteur, do not try to fool us. The method is absolutely useless!"

The scientist was now an old hand at battling to prove the truth of his scientific findings and he turned on public opinion with every tool at his command. He published a book, called *Studies in Wine,* in which he described his remedy so clearly that any wine maker could put it to use. He addressed scientific societies. He welcomed doubters to his lab, gave them treated wine to drink, and defied them to find any flaw in its taste. He requested that a commission of wine experts compare his heated products with unheated ones. Such a commission gathered at the École Normale and, like the doubters, finally admitted that, if any difference did exist in the taste, it was unnoticeable.

The years saw the gradual breakdown of resistance to his process. The last barrier of doubt was shattered in a test devised by the Minister of the Navy. This official had struggled for years to keep wine unspoiled on long ocean voyages and now he informed Louis that he planned to place bottles of treated wine aboard the frigate, *La Sibylle,* outbound on an around-the-world cruise. A second cargo—this one of untreated wine—was to be stored on a vessel making a short run to West Africa.

"Go right ahead," Louis said eagerly. "I know precisely what results you'll achieve."

His anticipations proved correct. The heated wines survived the long journey without spoiling. But the wine aboard the second ship went bad long before the coast of West Africa was sighted.

At last, Louis sat back, completely satisfied. Nothing more need be said. Wine producers everywhere, even in distant California, hailed him as the savior of their industry. All Europe talked of the little germs that had the power to make wines go bad, and of this fellow Pasteur who had controlled them.

Another giant step forward had been taken in the crusade to convince the world of the power of micro-organisms.

And, though Louis did not know it at the time, an even greater step forward had been taken in the never ending task of protecting the health of mankind. His heating process—which he was beginning to employ with vinegar—would someday be applied by scientists to milk and cream, and would shield countless children from disease.

They would know the process by the name "Pasteurization."

Louis had achieved success in one area. But he was threatened with failure in another.

His process for preventing the spread of pébrine among silkworms wasn't working properly. It wasn't working proerly at all.

He went down to Alais for the silkworm season of 1866, which lasted from February to June, and grimaced when the cultivators gathered in his makeshift lab. A few greeted him pleasantly. But the majority gave him an icy welcome. They entered on leaden feet and it was painfully evident that their distrust of his ability to wipe out the disease was greater than ever. Well, he couldn't blame them. They were desperate, facing ruin and poverty. He had been sent to help them and thus far, according to the reports he had received in Paris, it looked as if he hadn't done much good.

André, acting as spokesman for the group, repeated the bad news first seen in the reports. "We did exactly as you instructed. We threw away all the eggs with corpuscles and cultivated those without them, but all too often it did no good. Many of the worms that hatched out of the healthy eggs turned sick. They had pébrine—yet, *there wasn't a single corpuscle to be found in their bodies!*"

Louis flinched. He dropped his gaze to the stone floor. He couldn't bear to look at the squarish faces ranged round him, some eager with hope, most impassive with hostility. It hurt badly to have to confess, "I know. The very same thing happened to many of the worms I raised in my Paris lab."

Pébrine without corpuscles!

How that problem had haunted him these past months since he had first encountered it. He had lost sleep over it. He had paced his lab for hours at a time because of it. He had tried to solve it whenever the sick wines had given him a free moment. His every attempt had failed. Failed miserably.

"But how can there be pébrine without corpuscles?" André asked. "You yourself said you thought the corpuscles caused the disease."

Louis shrugged helplessly. "Well, perhaps I was wrong. Perhaps the corpuscles are merely a symptom of the disease and take quite a while to develop in some worms. There are many possibilities. I don't know which one is correct. I just don't know."

His gaze swept along the faces. He didn't like what he saw in the angry ones. There was hard self-satisfaction there, and he knew what their owners were thinking: it is just as we suspected—this Pasteur who is supposed to be so brilliant is really just a simpleton when it comes to pébrine; we've known this all along; now he has just admitted it himself.

Louis struck out at the self-satisfied expressions sharply. "But this I *do* know. If I'm given enough time, I can solve this thing. I'm sure I can. Have patience with me."

Have patience! The doubters snorted. He had made the

same request of them his last visit. They had complied. They had been patient; oh, so very patient. And what had happened? A whole year had been wasted fooling with a useless remedy.

"And just what will you be doing, Professor," one skeptic asked, "while we are being patient and our families are getting ready to go begging on the streets?"

There was but one thing he planned to do. Work. Study the disease day and night. Track down the mysterious reason why there should be pébrine without corpuscles.

He spent the next five months peering into his microscope, studying silkworms in every phase of their development. He investigated the eggs from which worms were hatched. Then he turned to worms that were mature and ready to spin their cocoons of silk. Next he concentrated on the cocoons in which the worms transformed themselves into moths. And, finally, he watched moths emerge from the cocoons and lay the new eggs that started all over again the life cycle of these strange little creatures.

All this study did not give him the answer he sought. But it revealed to him other important facts, facts that made his call to the cultivators at the end of the season a confident one.

"No," he replied to the question foremost in their minds as they formed a half-circle about him, "I still don't know why the corpuscles fail to appear in certain cases of pébrine. But I want to talk to you of other things. These things may enable us to halt the disease."

He turned to a work table. On it was a large tray full of tiny cocoons. "Before now, we've concentrated on the eggs. Now we must shift our concentration to a new place, for my studies this past season have shown me that pébrine does its greatest damage after the worms have spun their cocoons and are turning into moths."

He placed a cocoon in his palm and held it out to the cultivators. "At this point, the disease is at its height. It is very easy to see that a worm is sick, even though he may not reveal a single corpuscle. It is here—in the cocoon—that we must center our fight. We must halt pébrine here, before the moths have a chance to burst out of their cocoons and spread the disease themselves and in the eggs they lay."

He leaned his back against the work table and spoke slowly. He knew the doubters weren't going to like his next words. "Now, how are we going to carry out this fight? Well, I've worked out a new system for you—"

He got no further.

The reaction of many was just what he had expected.

Irritation flooded square faces. Hard, impatient glances were exchanged. Another system! The first one hadn't worked. What guarantee was there that a new one would succeed? They wanted something more definite than systems. They wanted a cure!

Louis went on calmly. "It's a very simple method. Your nursery is full of cocoons. You wonder if pébrine is hidden in any of them. Here's all you do. Just take a hundred moths and heat them to hasten their development. Then study them under the microscope. You will be able to see all the signs of the disease quite easily. If pébrine is there, throw the moths away. Don't allow them to give birth to diseased eggs."

Confusion joined the anger in the faces.

Wait a moment! Did this Pasteur say the moths were to be studied in a microscope?

"How do you expect us to do this?" one man demanded. "It's all well and fine for scientists to use the microscope. But we're silkworm raisers. We know nothing of microscopes. We'll never be able to use one."

"But you will," Louis insisted. "I'll teach you. There's nothing hard about it. My daughter, Marie-Louise, is only eight, but she already knows how to handle one perfectly."

He spent his last days at Alais instructing the cultivators in the use of the instrument. Then he distributed among them a batch of pure eggs he himself had prepared.

"Use the method I have given you," he told them, "and raise these worms carefully for next season. They have been prepared under the most rigid laboratory conditions possible, and I'm sure they'll show you my method is the right tool for the destruction of pébrine. We'll know for certain by this time next year."

"It had better work," one cultivator said grimly. "Otherwise, next season will be our last. But we'll wait and see what happens. We have no other choice."

Wait, wait, wait—

Train wheels, clattering over tracks pointing north, seemed to whisper that one word in Louis' ears all the way back to Paris. During the next months, he would continue his search for the reason why pébrine sometimes produced no corpuscles. But his chief job would be that of waiting—waiting to see if his method proved effective or if an entire industry collapsed.

Many tasks and honors filled the months that had to be lived until the next silkworm season. He resigned his directorship at the École Normale and accepted the position of Professor of Chemistry at the Sorbonne. He received the Grand Prix of the Exposition Internationale for his method of preserving wines by heating, and he went down to Orleans and addressed vinegar manufacturers on how this same heating process could insure the health of their own product.

The crowning event of the year was a week spent at the Palace of Compiègne as the guest of Napoleon III and Empress Eugénie. He attended the grand reception of the first evening with some uneasiness. Wherever he looked in the vast hall with its glittering chandeliers and polished floors, he saw the most famous men in Europe and their exquisitely dressed ladies.

"What am I doing here amid all this pomp and splendor?" the scientist asked himself with a wry smile. "I'm sure to do something silly out of sheer nervousness. I should be back in my lab this very minute; that's where I belong. Well, no matter. I'll wager I'm not even noticed among all the jewels and fine silks and medals and swords."

He soon knew he had guessed wrong, for he found himself confronted by the Emperor and being led from the other guests to a fireplace where he was dizzied with one question after another about his work. He began to relax and enjoy himself. Why, this man who stood before him, this man who ruled all France, was as eager in his quest of scientific knowledge as a schoolboy. Before he knew it, Louis was leaning easily against the mantle and quietly telling Napoleon III of such strange things as invisible giants, fermentations, and sick wines.

That same evening, after he had retired to his room,

Louis wrote to Paris for his microscope. He turned the rest of his visit into a long science lesson for Napoleon and Eugénie, much to their delight. While his fellow guests were touring the surrounding countryside, Louis scouted the imperial cellars and found eight bottles of diseased wine. He used these samples to acquaint the rulers with the types and causes of illness in wine.

At the end of one such meeting, held in private, Eugénie suddenly gripped Louis' microscope and swept into an adjoining room where the guests had assembled for early evening tea. She insisted that Louis repeat for them what he had just told his rulers, while she happily played the part of his assistant.

Only one mishap occurred during the entire visit, but it wasn't as upsetting as it was amusing. One of Louis' demonstrations had involved several live frogs. When he had finished with them, he packed them in a bag—that is, he packed them all away but one. This undetected escapee managed to make his way to Eugénie's bedroom. Late that night, the Empress, her regal foot quite bare, elected to step on the exact spot where he sat. Her shock and the rude blow her dignity suffered caused the Palace to rock with silent mirth for days to come, and Louis related the incident to Marie with a very red face.

Despite the honor of the Compiègne visit, life looked very bleak to Louis in 1867—very bleak indeed. Letters from the cultivators at Alais brought him bad news almost daily. The eggs he had prepared to prove the worth of his preventive method weren't turning out successfully.

"The worms are sickening and dying of pébrine," he said, waving one of the letters at Émile Duclaux. He couldn't hide his disgust. "But they're sickening and dying without showing a trace of corpuscles."

Why?

He travelled to Alais and locked himself in a small room of his lab there eighteen hours a day, away from Marie and Émile and everyone, in an attempt to answer that maddening one-word question. Disappointment was a scalding knot in his throat. He had counted so much on the eggs. Not an hour now passed in which he didn't tell himself he was sick to death of silkworms; that he wished he had never laid eyes on them; and that, if he didn't unravel this mystery soon, he'd chuck the whole lot of them right out the window.

But, always, he'd push such thoughts aside. He'd square his shoulders and place more noncorpuscular dead worms in his microscope. He stared at them until his eyes burned. They were black and shriveled. He held one between his fingers. It was soft and flaccid, like an empty bladder. He swung his eyes to little creatures not yet dead and watched them crawl sluggishly and tiredly over mulberry leaves.

"Bah!" he snorted in exasperation late one night. "There's no answer to this business." He glared at the shriveled beings in the tray. "How do I even know you have pébrine?"

The words had barely escaped his lips before his every muscle was rigid. His mouth became a thin, hard line. He had flung out the words as a bitter, meaningless joke. But now, as he thought about them, they took on a very deep, a very real meaning.

Was it possible that these worms—that all worms without corpuscles—were suffering from some disease other than pébrine?

That might be the solution to the whole problem.

He groaned.

Why hadn't he thought of it before?

Was it because it was too simple an answer to such a complex mystery?

Was it because he had been too sure he was dealing with pébrine alone?

Was it because he knew too little of silkworms in the first place?

He shrugged off the questions. This was not the time for wondering. This was the time to check all the books and papers on maladies of silkworms that he could locate. In such books—in explanations of little-known experiments— he found the answer to two years of bewilderment.

The answer drove him from behind his locked door to the outer room of the lab. He threw himself into a chair and waved Émile Duclaux to his side. He had never felt so tired and so angry in all his life. Tears stood high in his eyes and his voice was a cracked thing as he said:

"Nothing has been accomplished. There are two diseases!"

His head twisted from side to side in agony. Two years of life had been completely wasted. Two years of travel and work and enduring the distrust of the cultivators had gone for nothing.

"Yes, there are two diseases," he told Émile, whose face was now a picture of amazement. "Pébrine and a sickness called 'flacherie.' All the worms with corpuscles have pébrine. All those without them are suffering from flacherie. It's caused by several types of bacteria that attack the intestines of the worms. Oh, I've been so stupid! I should have long ago recognized the fact that there were two diseases."

"You haven't been stupid," Émile said. His voice was gentle and sharp all at the same time. "It's just that you've had no experience with flacherie."

Louis raised a haggard face. "But I shall have much experience with it from now on. We shall have to start all over again." He pounded a fist into his open palm. "All over again! We're right back where we were two years ago. Only now we have to fight two diseases." His head came forward and he stared at the floor. He wondered if he had the strength left to fight two diseases.

He pulled himself to his feet. It didn't matter that he was close to exhaustion. All that mattered was that this silkworm nightmare be ended once and for all.

He started his studies all over again and soon found that his methods for curbing pébrine worked perfectly when dealing with that disease alone. This knowledge heartened him and he went on to develop a preventive method against flacherie. It involved the use of the microscope.

At the end of the 1867 silkworm season he demonstrated the process to cultivators. First, he taught them how to recognize the symptoms and bacteria of flacherie. Then he opened a moth and picked up a scalpel.

"With this instrument, extract a small portion of the intestinal cavity." His careful actions matched his words. He mixed the extracted matter in water. "Now examine it in a microscope. If you find that the micro-organisms of flacherie are not present in a number of moths, then you may consider that the whole strain from which they came is suitable for breeding. But, if the micro-organisms are present, destroy the entire strain."

The knowledge that he was dealing with two diseases enabled him to produce absolutely pure eggs in his lab.

He gave them to the cultivators to be used for the 1868 season.

"You can depend on these eggs," he told them. "Healthy worms will come from them. There'll be no pébrine among them—and no flacherie."

The 1868 season proved to Louis that the silkworm battle was almost over. The eggs hatched out healthy worms, and the cultivators, by using his methods, were able to hold illness among the little creatures to its lowest point in years. Louis' face was deeply lined with fatigue, but he smiled broadly. Gone at last was the distrust of the cultivators. They now welcomed him to Alais as one of their own. The disappearance of their stony expressions meant as much to the scientist as did the beginning of the retreat of pébrine and flacherie.

But, though the battle was nearly over, Louis could not rest. There was still much to be done. He responded to the frantic calls of cultivators in the Pyrenees and Alps, and traveled to their nurseries to install his preventive measures. He began assembling the material for two books he would soon write on the diseases of the silkworms.

And victory over the diseases of the silkworms could not be his without last-minute troubles. He had to endure the rage of unscrupulous silkworm egg dealers who didn't care a jot if they sold cultivators healthy or unhealthy eggs. They didn't like it one bit when they learned their eggs were to be examined microscopically before purchase, and they concocted all sorts of slanderous rumors about Louis' character and work. The rumors succeeded in making their way into the newspapers. One paper reported that Louis had been stoned out of Alais by a group of infuriated citizens.

At the same time, the scientist found himself involved in

a nasty fight with the French government. The scuffle had nothing to do with silkworms. Louis, thoroughly annoyed by the meager facilities in which he had long worked, resolutely set out to obtain funds with which to build a new and bigger lab. The government showed itself reluctant to provide such monies and Louis took his anger—the anger of all French scientists—to the lecture platform and magazines, stating heatedly, "Physicists and chemists without laboratories are like soldiers without arms on the battlefield." The struggle was a long, bitter one, but it was finally resolved by Napoleon III himself. The Emperor, deeply impressed by the scientist during Pasteur's visit at Compiègne, ordered that the laboratory which Louis desired be built for him in the garden of the École Normale. Napoleon set aside 30,000 francs of his own household money for the task.

Louis could scarce believe his ears. After all the years of working in cramped quarters with faulty equipment, he was at last to have the space he so badly needed. He immediately set about the job of designing his new quarters.

All his assorted labors caused the Pasteur family to watch Louis with growing alarm. He was so nervous and tired looking. They were certain he was straining his health beyond the breaking point.

Their fears were well grounded, for, on October 19, 1868, the exhausted Louis felt a strange prickling sensation along his left side. He ignored it all through the morning, but it turned into a violent shivering which forced him to lie down after lunch. Had Marie had her way, he would have remained in bed. But he was scheduled to address the Academy of Sciences and insisted on leaving the house.

He managed to reach home after the meeting and moved

on unsteady legs to his bed. "I'm just tired," he told himself as he drew the covers about his shoulders. "A good night's rest will take care of everything." But, a few moments later, the tingling and shivering of earlier in the day returned. Fear closed over him. He tried to call for Marie, but could not fashion a single word. At last, he managed a cry for help. Marie rushed to his side. She took just one brief look at him and immediately summoned an old family friend, Dr. Godelier, to the house.

By the time the physician arrived, Louis was the prisoner of a recurring paralysis. For long minutes at a time, it deprived him of his speech and caused him to lose control of the muscles along his left side. Then it would release him for a short while. In those moments when he was free of the suffocating weight that rendered his muscles useless, he described his own symptoms in a hoarse whisper. Dr. Godelier drew Marie to one side.

What he told her softly washed all color from her face. "It's a cerebral hemorrhage."

A white-knuckled fist jumped to her mouth. She fell back a step, then steadied herself. Molten steel seemed to flow through her body. "Will he live?"

Godelier shook his head. "I don't know. We can only hope."

Late next night, Godelier and Marie had abandoned whatever hope they had held. Both were certain the end was at hand. Louis was intensely cold and weak. His eyes were languid. He tossed uncomfortably and groaned of his paralyzed arm, "It is like lead; if only it could be cut off."

Marie turned away to hide her tears. An icy voice somewhere inside her whispered she would be telling her son and daughter before dawn that their father was gone. But Louis survived the night and the next day and then the next. For seven days he hovered on the brink of death and then strength began to seep back into his tortured body.

It was a time of great but quiet activity in the Pasteur home. Students of the École Normale and the most distinguished men of French science came together to sit at his bed and urge him back to health. He astonished them all. Whenever he was able to talk, he insisted on discussing his work.

One scientist, M. Gernez, spent the major part of one evening attempting to divert the sick man's mind from that work. But Louis would not be diverted, and Gernez finally abandoned his efforts and wrote down word-for-word everything Pasteur said. When he showed the result to Dumas, the latter sighed with relief.

"He's going to be all right. Last week a stroke almost killed him. This week he has dictated a brilliant and clear note on a new method for discovering flacherie in silkworm eggs." Dumas' smile was a trembling thing. "Yes, he's going to be all right. I think I can sleep in peace again."

The construction of the new École Normale lab had commenced just before Louis' illness. Now he asked time and again how the work was progressing. Each question received from Marie the vague reply that all was going well. His wife's eyes refused to meet his and he suspected that all was *not* going well. He had another reason for thinking things amiss. His room overlooked the École Normale Garden and the air should have been riddled with the sounds of clanking barrows and pounding hammers. But not a single noise came from that direction. Louis raised himself to glance out the window. What he saw caused him to call his good friend, the distinguished soldier, General Fave, to his room.

"Work on the lab has stopped."

"Nonsense," said Fave as soothingly as possible.

"I've seen it with my own eyes. There was but one workman over there today, and he was doing nothing. I know what's going on. The government fully expects me to die. And what is the use of putting up a fine building for a man who will never use it?" He shook a finger at the elderly soldier. "My friend, please tell the government that I plan to go on living for years. And tell the government I shall need my new lab very soon."

Fave nodded with an admiring smile. "I shall be most happy to take your words directly to the Emperor himself."

Fave bowed out of the room and several days later the Minister of Public Instruction received the following note:

My dear M. Duruy:

I have heard that—unknown to you probably—the men who were working at M. Pasteur's laboratory were kept away from the very day he became ill; he has been much affected by this circumstance, which seemed to point to his non-recovery. I beg you will issue orders that the work begun should be continued. Believe in my sincere friendship—Napoleon.

As the Emperor had requested, work was begun again— *immediately.*

By November of 1868, Louis was again dining downstairs. By December, he was eager to be back at his work. In January, 1869, he was permitted to resume his silkworm studies at St. Hippolyte le Fort, near Alais.

"Is it wise for him to return to work so soon?" Marie asked Dr. Godelier.

"No," Godelier admitted. "But it is less wise to have him brooding about the house because he has nothing to do."

Back at work, Louis found that, though the cultivators now trusted him completely, there remained some official skepticism of his methods. For instance, the Lyons Silk Commission doubted the dependability of his processes and asked him to send to them for their study a batch of healthy eggs he had produced. To prove that he could personally control and guarantee the outcome of any eggs he produced, he sent them four lots and made the following bold predictions:

1. One lot will produce healthy worms.
2. One lot will perish exclusively from *pébrine*.
3. One lot will perish exclusively from *flacherie*.
4. One lot will perish partly from *pébrine* and partly from *flacherie*.

All his predictions came true and were recorded in the minutes of the Commission. In Lyons official doubt of his methods was thus quickly abolished.

Then he learned that the French government was reluctant to sanction his preventive measures; political reasons were behind their hesitancy. They seesawed back and forth over the matter of the sanction until a long-time admirer of the scientist and Minister of the Emperor's Household, Marshall Vaillant, arranged to send Louis to the Villa Vincentina, near Trieste.

The property, owned by the imperial family, was the site of a silkworm nursery that had fallen into decay because of pébrine and flacherie. While the fine climate restored his health, Louis installed his preventive measures there and brought the nursery back to active use. As a result of his work, the nursery showed a profit of 22,000 francs, the first profit it had evidenced in ten years. The success with the nursery did much to hasten the government in sanctioning Louis' methods.

The year 1869 brought the silkworm study to a close. Louis looked back over the past years with mingled satisfaction and sorrow. They had brought him tragedy—the deaths of his daughters and his own illness. And they had brought him failure. He would never forget the dismal moments when he had thought the silkworm mystery was beyond solution.

But, finally, the years had brought him grand success. They had witnessed the destruction of the diseases of the wines and then the silkworms. Not a day passed without bringing him some word of the growing prosperity of two industries that had seemed all but dead.

He closed his eyes for a moment.

He had won his battles with disease and he had outlived tragedy.

Surely, the coming years would bring peace and happiness.

The Dark Years

"I'm sure," Louis told Marie at the family dinner on January 1, 1870, "that this year is going to be a good one for us."

He had every reason for such a belief. He was fully recovered from his illness; an annoying limp and a fatigue that came upon him easily were all that remained of it. The new École Normale lab was complete, and wine manufacturers and silkworm cultivators throughout France continued to hail him as the one responsible for the fresh prosperity their industries were realizing. He was as successful as a man could hope to be at forty-eight.

"Yes," he went on confidently, "the bad times are past."

Seven months later, he looked back on that confidence and called it a miserable, hollow thing. The bad times had really just begun, for, on July 19, the Franco-Prussian War burst over his head with the blinding suddenness of a flash of lightning. A diplomatic move, designed by France to halt the expansion of German power, had infuriated the Prussian king. A series of angry telegrams had passed between the two governments and had resulted in a declaration of war by France. Now proud German regiments were pounding their boots into French soil.

The École Normale became a silent place. When Louis walked along its corridors all he heard were the lonely echoes of his own footsteps. Every student had vanished in the rush to enlist in the army. His own son, Jean-Baptiste, was now at the front with General Bourbaki's famed army.

Louis couldn't stand the loneliness of the school. He couldn't stand the quiet of the house without the laughter of the tall, erect Jean-Baptiste. And, above all, he couldn't stand the dread news of continuing German victories on the French border. He knew that he, too, must defend his country alongside his son and the boys who had been his students so recently. He did his best to conceal his limp as he walked into a nearby recruiting station.

The officer in charge, a long straw of a man, greeted him with a glance that ran from his bad leg to his graying hair.

"How old are you, Monsieur? Fifty?"

Louis glared at him defiantly. "Forty-eight."

"And your leg—have you injured it?"

"No. I suffered a stroke almost two years ago. But it was nothing. I'm in perfect health. I can carry a gun as well as anyone. It is my leg that bothers me, not my hands and arms."

The officer shook his head. "I'm sorry, Monsieur. It is impossible for the French army to use your services."

So! His country's army thought he couldn't be of use. It thought he was fit only to sit at home and await the letters of Jean-Baptiste or walk the empty halls of the École Normale and hear the lonely echoes. Well, there *was* one thing he could do. He snatched from the wall of his study the framed honorary diploma of Doctor of Medicine the University of Bonn had awarded him two years ago. His pen was alive with anger as he wrote the head of the Bonn Medical School:

"I am led by my conscience to request that you efface my name from the archives of your university, and to take back that diploma, as a sign of indignation inspired in a French chemist by the barbarity and hypocrisy of him (the German war leader, Bismarck) who, for the satisfaction of his criminal pride, persists in the massacre of two great nations."

He shoved both diploma and letter into a large envelope and mailed them to Germany.

The passing days of the war continued to become more unbearable, and communiques from every front more grim. The French were being driven back on every battle line. Louis could no longer bear to drag himself to the École Normale. The school had been turned into a hospital and, whenever he went there, he felt utterly useless. He was not a medical doctor and was incapable of doing a thing to alleviate the suffering of the young men who tossed in pain on their cots.

Then came the worst news of all. The Germans were sweeping toward Paris and the city would soon be under siege. Louis clenched his fists. "Now I'll fight," he promised himself. Every citizen, no matter what his age and health, would be needed to defend the city.

But Marie and his old friend Pierre Bertin argued vehemently against his resolve. "You must leave, Louis. France can't afford to lose a scientist of your caliber in the fighting. You'll be needed again after the war." After much plead-

ing, they convinced him of the soundness of their reasoning
and he departed with Marie for Arbois on September 5,
1870. Tears stood high in his eyes for his endangered city on
the Seine.

His stay at Arbois was a miserable, restless one. He had
no place to work. And he had no will to work, for news of
the war was worse than ever. French soldiers died wherever
they met the Germans and their modern, polished weapons.
And news of Jean-Baptiste? Marie and Louis had received
not a letter from him in more than a month. This, and the
information that General Bourbaki's army was suffering a
terrible defeat near the town of Hericourt, filled them with
black fear. They were certain their son was lying dead or
injured somewhere in the snow. They knew they couldn't
stand the loss of yet another of their children, and their
anguish drove them to an insane plan.

They would go in search of Jean-Baptiste! They would
find him and take him away from war and death!

And so on a Tuesday morning, January 24, 1871, they
drove a rickety carriage eastward out of Arbois. With them
was their daughter Marie-Louise. Their route took them
toward the city of Pontilier. What they saw appalled them.
The snow-covered road was choked with French soldiers
retreating from the battle. Some of them shouted to the
carriage for food. Others were too exhausted even to raise
their eyes. All of them wore filthy, tattered uniforms that
gave them no protection from the piercing cold. In the distance could be heard the frightening rumble of artillery.

They stopped for the night in the town of Montrond.
Wherever they looked, they saw soldiers rolled in thin
blankets and sleeping in the mud or kneeling close to small

fires. Others lurched about in search of a bit of straw on which to sleep. Many had taken refuge in a church. They sat before the altar and attempted to bandage frozen feet. All were starving.

Throughout the town Louis limped, asking over and over again the pathetic question, "Have you seen Sergeant Pasteur?"

For the most part, he received only blank stares in return. A few soldiers managed to shake their heads. And fewer still managed to whisper the single, heartbreaking word, "No."

The next day, the carriage, now little more than a wreck, was back on the road to Pontalier. Reaching that town, Louis sighted a group of soldiers huddled about a fire.

"Have you seen Sergeant Pasteur?" he asked them.

One of the men lifted a haggard face to him. He had trouble forming his words. "Sergeant Pasteur? Yes . . . Yes, I think I saw him just last night."

Louis thought his heart had stopped beating.

"Where?"

Seconds were required for the soldier to make his exhausted brain work. "On the road to Chaffois. . . . You'll find that road on the far side of town."

"Was he—was he injured?" Louis' face was a blank mask as he waited for the reply.

"No, Monsieur."

Relief flooded the scientist.

The soldier went on struggling to talk. "At least, he seemed all right last night." He gestured vaguely, hopelessly. "But, for all I know, he may be dead by now."

Louis thanked the soldier and, filled with both dread and hope, searched out the road to Chaffois. It was now nothing

more than a mire of crushed snow and mud. Louis spent
the day wondering how many mud holes the carriage could
survive before falling apart. Evening was at hand when he
saw a farm wagon stalled at the side of the road.

He patted Marie's hand encouragingly and descended to
the snow. He limped to the wagon and called up to the
driver.

"Have you seen Sergeant Pasteur?" How often had he
asked that terrible question in the past hours?

The driver regarded him as if he were something from
another world. His eyes seemed to ask, "What are you doing
out here in that snow in that wreck of a carriage? Why
isn't a man of your age safe at home in front of a fire?"
Aloud, he said, "I'm sorry, Monsieur. I do not know a
Sergeant Pasteur."

Another disappointment. Louis lowered his gaze and
started back to the carriage and the anxious faces of Marie
and Marie-Louise.

Suddenly a voice halted him.

"Father! Father!"

It was a hoarse cry from the back of the wagon. He spun
about in time to see one soldier among many lifting himself
from the blackened straw. The soldier was a scarecrow of
a man. His uniform was torn almost to rags. His face was
streaked with mud and hadn't felt a razor for days, but Louis
ran to him with tears streaming from his eyes. Jean-Baptiste
dropped from the wagon, and father and son embraced each
other there in the mud of the road while the wagon driver
regarded them with astonished eyes.

Louis placed the boy in the carriage and the torturous
return to Arbois was made. There, Marie and Louis watched
his slow return to health. Their journey had been an ordeal

they would never forget. But it had been worth every terrible moment. Their only son had been spared from death. They soon knew he would never need return to the horrors of battle again, for the war came to a dismal end just before the beginning of February, 1871, and long before the boy was fully recovered.

France, crushed by Germany, now had to live through a brief socialist revolution. Louis, eager to return to his work and angered by the presence of German occupation troops in Arbois, was tempted to accept an offer from the Italian government to assist silkworm cultivators at Pisa. He finally decided to remain in France and wipe out the bad fermentations in beer.

His French pride led him to this decision. Even if France had lost the war, he could do his utmost to make his nation's beers superior to those of the Germans, considered the finest in the world. This work, which lasted from 1871 to 1877, was pursued at a small brewery near Chamalières and at the laboratory of Émile Duclaux who was now performing researches of his own; it even took him to the large breweries in London. He found, just as he had expected, that the bad fermentations were caused by the growth of micro-organisms in the beer yeast. Back in Paris at last, he destroyed the organisms by heating bottled beer to a temperature of fifty to fifty-five degrees centigrade, just as he had done with wine. The process, now called *pasteurizing,* resulted in French beers that were on a par with those of Germany. When the Congress of French Brewers met in 1889 they gave Louis full credit for the improvement seen in their products.

Life brought him two delights during these years. In

1863, though he was not a physician, he was elected to the
Academy of Medicine in Paris; and, in 1874, the French National Assembly voted him a grant of twelve thousand francs
a year with which to carry on his researches. How wonderful all this was! He now had sufficient funds to maintain
his lab and employ needed additional assistants, among
them two brilliant young men, Émile Roux and Charles
Chamberland. And he now had the chance to take his ideas
concerning the importance of the little germs in the world
directly to medical doctors.

One of the chief ideas he placed before the Academy of
Medicine had been with him for years. It was the deep con-
viction that micro-organisms caused disease in humans, just
as they caused fermentations. "Look for the germs, the bugs,"
he lectured the doctors. "Wipe them out or at least avoid
them and you'll avert much sickness, infection, and death."
But he soon found that the doctors did not want to heed
his words. They were a proud lot and were quite certain
that a "mere chemist"—that is what they called him—
could not have any medical theories worth hearing. Their
attitude seemed to say, "You take care of your test tubes
and we'll attend to the illnesses of the world."

"Do you know what they tell me?" he asked Émile Roux
and Charles Chamberland one morning. "They tell me that
diseases and infections are caused by some mysterious force
within the body of a person or an animal. They tell me
there is no connection between the germs and sickness. Why,
they are no more advanced than the people of ancient times
who thought that disease was an evil spirit that entered the
body. Oh, they are so blind."

Roux and Chamberland, both dark haired and good looking, agreed. They had visited Paris hospitals with Louis and they knew them to be places of death. There was a saying in Paris at the time that to go to a hospital was just about the same as committing suicide. And the assistants had heard Louis repeat so many times, "What else can one expect? Doctors and nurses fail to wash their hands before an operation. No one ever thinks to cleanse a surgical instrument. Bandages are handled carelessly and left unchanged too long. Wards are not cleaned properly. The germs cannot help but be everywhere, carrying disease to every corner, settling in wounds and infecting them."

One ray of hope could be seen amidst all this tragedy. In Scotland, a Dr. Joseph Lister heard of Louis' ideas and did something about them. In all his operations, he insisted that every instrument be sterilized with carbolic acid and that the hands of the doctors and nurses be thoroughly washed. He saw to it that bandages were very carefully prepared, that the patient was placed on clean linen, and that a gauze shield was constructed around the open wound to purify the air near it. The results he obtained heartened Lister and made many a doubting physician sit up and take notice. Within two years, he had reduced the fatalities in his surgical cases from ninety-five per cent to fifteen per cent.

Louis was delighted when, in February of 1874, he received a letter from Dr. Lister that read in part:

Allow me to take this opportunity to tender you my most cordial thanks for having, by your brilliant researches, demonstrated to me the truth of the germ theory of putrefaction, and thus furnished me with the principle upon which alone the antiseptic system can be carried out. Should you at any time visit Edinburgh, it would, I believe, give you sincere gratification to see at our hospital how largely mankind is being benefited by your labours.

I need hardly add that it would afford me the highest gratification to show you how greatly surgery is indebted to you.

Louis reread the letter happily. The pain he had felt when the doctors at the Academy of Medicine had ignored his ideas eased a bit. At least, one person—though he was in a foreign land—had proved those ideas worthy. Surely more and more physicians would become convinced of their truth.

And more *were* convinced. Lister's techniques spread first to Germany and then to parts of France. A few of the younger doctors at the Academy began to employ the antiseptic method of surgery and credited Louis for inspiring it with his constant preaching of the little germs. But the pompous ones, the self-important medicos, were still far from convinced. The only thing they seemed to believe was that a "mere chemist" had no business sticking his nose into medical affairs.

Louis' tours of Paris hospitals with Roux and Chamberland brought him to grips with an illness called puerperal—or childbirth—fever. A disease that struck new mothers, it had, in 1864 alone, claimed the lives of more than three hundred women in the Paris Maternity Hospitals. Louis' microscope showed him that the sickness was always accompanied by small rounded germs that, clinging to each other, resembled long strings of beads. He was certain these micro-organisms were responsible for the fever.

At one meeting of the Academy he listened to a noted

physician lecture on several popular theories concerning the cause of the disease. Louis stirred impatiently, then angrily. The well-dressed medical man was very eloquent. He was very learned. He was very dignified. But he was absolutely wrong!

Suddenly, Louis found himself on his feet. He limped to the platform and saw the doctor's face redden as the lecture was interrupted by the shout, "You're talking nonsense! Childbirth fever isn't caused by any of the things you've mentioned. Here! I'll show you the real villains!"

He snatched up a piece of chalk and drew on a blackboard the string-of-beads micro-organisms. "There! They're the cause of the fever! The doctors and nurses and surgical instruments carry them to the patient."

He saw the look of shock spread from the lecturer's face to the audience. He heard some of the younger physicians applaud him, but the applause was drowned by the shouts of the pompous and tight-minded ones who jumped to their feet, gesticulating wildly and talking all at once.

"Sit down!"

"Get off that platform! How dare you interrupt the speaker!"

"You've no right to tell *us* about disease and surgery."

Louis gripped the speaker's table and thrust his face toward the audience. His eyes wanted to see every face at once. His voice wanted to enter every brain. Perhaps he could turn this from a moment of turmoil to the moment when he at last convinced them of how blind and backward they were.

"I've all the right in the world to tell you about the little germs," he shouted. "I've studied them for fourteen years. I know what they can do. Can't you understand that simple fact?" His voice was full of pleading. "I know they are giants for good and evil. In this case, they're evil. But they can be wiped out. Your hospitals can be free of them. Wash your hands, your sponges, your surgical instruments. Do as Lister does! That will kill the little bugs. That will kill infection and prevent the spread of disease!"

But the tight-minded doctors wouldn't listen, as usual. They drove him from the platform with their shouts and their insults.

"Take your germs back to your lab."

"Look at them all you like, but don't bother us with them. They're much too small to be of any consequence."

"And stop trying to be a doctor."

"Leave medicine to those who know something about it."

Louis left the Academy in a cold fury. Perhaps he would not have been so angry had he known that one day the importance of germs in medicine would be recognized throughout the world; that one day Joseph Lister's surgical techniques would be applied in hospitals everywhere; that one day, when germs were killed through sterilization, infections and disease such as childbirth fever would all but disappear. But for now he could only face Roux and Chamberland with the heated words:

"I've tried to tell the doctors that germs are the key to disease. Most of them won't believe me. Now I'm going to *show* them I speak the truth!"

Yes, he would show them. He had the money and the help to do so; besides Roux and Chamberland, he had quite enough other assistants for the job. He knew his life had reached an important turning point. There would be little time now for crystallography and fermentations. All his attention would turn to disease and its germs. He would fight every disease of man and animal he could find, starting with those that afflicted animals.

He knew he was at last starting to keep the promise he had made himself at the graves of little Jeanne, Cécile, and Camille.

CHAPTER
12

Anthrax and
Chicken Cholera

"I've never seen this lab in such a state," Émile Roux
sighed one morning in 1878. "Soon there will be no room in
it for human beings!"

Indeed, it was in a state. Though the main room was
dotted with test tubes and apparatus for Louis' newest spontaneous generation and fermentation experiments, the whole
place might have been easily mistaken for a menagerie.

Along one wall of a side room, lab workers hovered over
sheep in pens. Some of the fleecy animals moved about play-
fully, bumping into each other, bleating and dipping their
noses into feed pails. Others lay on their sides and stared
up at the workers out of drowsy, pain-wracked eyes. They
were victims of a disease that was destroying the livelihood
of thousands of French farmers—anthrax.

Directly across the room were two round cages with black
metal tops. The more timid of the workers stepped past

these cages quickly, nervously, for housed within were two large dogs that growled incessantly and sometimes threw themselves against the steel bars savagely while greenish spittle drained from their lips and their eyes bleared and rolled with a dizzying madness. Brought to the lab by the veterinarian, Doctor Bourrel, they were suffering from rabies. One glimpse of their kind on a city street or a country road had the power to terrorize the bravest of men. A single bite from one such animal usually resulted in an agony of fever and choking thirst. A world that knew the horrors of cholera and the Black Plague readily admitted there was no worse death than that brought about by hydrophobia.

Yes, the lab was in a state, but it was living proof that Louis was keeping his promise to his three little girls.

The first of the diseases he attacked was the deadly anthrax. Often called charbon or splenic fever, it had plagued agriculturists for years beyond recall. It caused a loss of several million francs annually in France alone. Horses, cows, sheep, and, more terrible, even humans fell prey to it. On some farms, it destroyed more than twenty out of every one hundred sheep. It had the ability to make farmers distrust the very land on which they lived, for there were everywhere "cursed fields" and "dangerous mountains" where animals could not graze without contracting the disease.

"Drooping heads, shaking limbs, and gasping breath," Louis told his assistants at the very outset of their study, "they're the major symptoms."

"And the result is death within a few hours," Charles Chamberland put in. "Often before a farmer or shepherd even notices his animals are ill."

Louis ran his finger down a page of notes he had made on the initial scientific investigations into the disease. These young men had to learn all there was to know about anthrax before they could even think of attacking it. "What causes the disease? That's what we want to know; and the sooner the better. Davaine and Royer, two of this country's finest scientists, did some anthrax research several years ago. They found microscopic, rodlike things in the blood of dead sheep. Davaine called these little rods 'bacteria' and came to the conclusion they were the anthrax killers."

"Yes," Émile Roux said. "I remember reading of his experiment. It's been called a classic piece of laboratory work. He inoculated rabbits with the blood of sheep and they all took sick and died. Then he removed the rods from the blood by passing it through a filter. The rabbits he next inoculated with the filtered blood refused to contract anthrax. He was convinced the disease wouldn't appear without the rods."

"But other scientists contradicted his findings with theories of their own and the cause of anthrax continued to be a mystery," Louis said. He tapped the paper. "Then along came the German, Robert Koch, and his discovery. He sighted little oval bodies, which he called 'spores,' in the blood of diseased animals when the rods could not be seen. Just two years ago, after experimenting with some mice, he claimed that *both* the rods and spores cause anthrax."

Chamberland grinned. "I know the rest of the story. He was opposed by a number of researchers who preached that the disease is actually brought on by some 'unknown substance' and that the rods and spores merely accompany it."

Louis' shrug was one of resignation. "And so it is as always. There are all sorts of theories, but not one definite conclusion. The true anthrax killer remains unknown."

Obviously, his first task was to find which of the three—the rods, the spores, or the "unknown substance"—was the guilty party. He suspected the rods and spores. But suspicions alone were valueless. He needed proof.

He began his detective work by preparing a clear solution into which he placed but a mere drop of blood from an animal with anthrax. In a matter of hours, his microscope showed him that the solution was teeming with the rods and spores. What a magnificent, spine-tingling sight they were! They did not remain the stubby little things Davaine and Royer had seen; as they grew, they became long, worm-like beings that tangled themselves into intricate, shivering webs. Webs of living thread. That's what they looked like. How easily they made you forget you were tired! How easily they made you forget all the other work that awaited your attention!

At hand now was the critical phase of his experiment—the phase that would focus the light of guilt on the rods and spores or prove them innocent.

Louis extracted a drop of the fluid and deposited it in a second solution. Then a drop of this weaker mixture went into a third flask. All of one day and the next he spent transplanting weaker and weaker drops in fresh solutions until forty transfers had been made and he was satisfied—bone weary but satisfied. Only the rods and spores remained. All other substances had been diluted right down to nothing.

His next step was to inoculate rabbits and guinea pigs with the diluted mixtures. "Let the animals become sick," he murmured to himself, "And I'll know the rods and spores are the guilty parties." If the animals remained healthy, then he would have to admit that some other substance—some unknown substance that had been diluted out of the solutions—was the villain.

His first series of inoculations told him he need look no further. All the rabbits and guinea pigs immediately fell ill and died. The endless prattle about "unknown substances" could be forgotten. He had found his guilty parties. They were the rods and spores.

It was a fine discovery. It earned him the praise of many scientists and, a sure sign of its great value, the jealousy of others. But it did nothing to reveal to him a method for preventing anthrax.

The end of the anthrax battle had to wait for a discovery that was to be made during another study.

One morning in 1879 Louis limped over a muddy track to the henhouse of a farm outside Paris. At his side was a chunky, stoop-shouldered man in heavy brown trousers, woolen shirt, and black boots.

"You haven't moved them at all?" Louis asked.

"No, Monsieur. I knew you were visiting Jacques' farm about this same matter and so I left them as I found them until I could fetch you here." The farmer tried to speak without emotion. After all, hardship was the lot of his profession. Crop failures and rain at the wrong time; crafty market men who tried to cheat you. But he couldn't hide his anger. "It's terrible, Monsieur! How is a man supposed to go on?"

They reached the henhouse, a thing of warped boards slanting against the flaking building the farmer called home.

He pulled the door open and Louis stepped into the gloomy interior. His eyes went immediately to a row of nests along the far wall. He saw motionless lumps of white feathers and braced himself for the farmer's words. He knew them well. He'd heard them so often these past days.

"Six of my best hens. Fine layers, all of them. One of them my little girl's pet." Yes, the same words as always. "Last night they were perfectly fine. In perfect health, I tell you. And then this morning . . ."

"I know," Louis said quietly. "If it is any consolation, my friend, you are not alone in this thing. May I see the rest of your birds?"

"They're not much better," the farmer said. He stuffed his hands in his pockets and led the way to a fenced area behind the house. He stood with his head down and one boot toe kicking the mud while Louis stepped to a low fence for a better view of the chickens within. "They're alive," was the farmer's only comment. "That's all I can say for them."

Louis nodded. There was no mistaking the fact that the birds were the sudden victims of chicken cholera. All the symptoms were here—the motionlessness of some of the animals, the staggering of others, the ruffed up feathers and drooping heads of all. Over in a corner, one hen moved about sluggishly, ignoring altogether her brood of chicks. In other parts of the yard, apparently healthy birds pecked away at grains of feed. They, too, would be caught by this same drowsiness today or, at latest, tomorrow.

"Look!" The farmer gave an agonized cry. Louis turned to him, then back to the yard again, following the direction of the man's pointing finger. Right against the henhouse wall was what had been a magnificent bird, the farmer's prize rooster. It was on its side, its usually heaving breast still, its once proud claws and strutting legs resembling limp yellow branches in the mud.

Again Louis turned to the farmer. The farmer was speaking to him, but the eyes in the pale, lined face were elsewhere. They were moving angrily back and forth across the yard and always coming to painful rest on the dead rooster. "What are you going to do about this, Professor?"

Oh, how many times he had heard that question in the past days? How many variations?

What are you going to do?

What can you do?

Can you cure this thing?

Will you?

Is it possible something can be done?

You will at least try, won't you?

And what was the answer? The lab was groaning under the current work load. Roux and Chamberland and all the others had forgotten what it was like to have a day off. And he himself—ever since the stroke, he had had to fight off an ever-nagging weariness. He wondered if he could bear the strain of still another problem, still another sickness to fight.

But, on the other hand, there were the statistics he had read in the past weeks. This malady, this cholera, had plagued farmers for centuries. When it struck their flocks, silently and without warning, they could count on the death of ninety per cent of their birds. To the poultry raiser, this was disaster, ruin.

So of what matter was a limp or a little fatigue or a little more work in the face of such statistics?

"I don't know what I can do," Louis said. "I only know that I can try to do something."

Émile sensed trouble when Louis thrust his way into the lab that afternoon. Maybe it was the way the scientist held his jaw—defiantly, stubbornly. Maybe it was the hard, uneven sound of his footsteps. Maybe it was the way he called, "Roux! Chamberland! I want to see you in the animal room." It was not the voice of one inviting you to a tea party.

The young men found Louis pacing up and down in front of the steel cages. His hands were clasped behind his back and the dogs might have been on another planet for all the attention he gave their snarling. He moved to the sheep pens, measured the wall behind them with his eyes and grunted something that sounded like, "Yes, yes, right here should do just fine."

Émile nudged Chamberland. "I'll wager you two francs we're going to have chicken cholera on our hands. I've suspected so ever since Toussaint interested him in it."

"No, thank you." Chamberland grinned knowingly.

Over his shoulder, Louis instructed, "Émile, I want you to have these pens moved—just a few feet will do. And, Chamberland, you will superintend the building of racks for nests to be placed in the newly opened space, please."

"I knew it," Émile murmured.

"So did I," Chamberland shot back out of the corner of his mouth. "I've been around here long enough to recognize all the signs of a new job, too."

Louis faced his assistants. "What's all this talk?"

The young men smiled innocently. "Not a thing, sir," Émile said. And then they were gone to do his bidding. He smiled after them. He had heard their every word. He thought they must know him so well that they had made

up a hundred little jokes about his mannerisms and eccen-
tricities. Well, that was to be expected of young people. He
recalled how he used to amuse Auguste Laurent and himself
with recitals of the fantastic things Balard might have carried in the giant pockets of his work smock. Ah, he had
traveled a long, hard road since those good days.

"Stop this useless reminiscing," he scolded himself.
"There's work to be done."

The first step in that work was to acquaint Roux and
Chamberland with all the known facts of the disease. He
showed them the classic symptoms to be found in the
chickens brought to the lab by farmers, then led them to a
microscope and instructed, "Look long at those little germs.
They were taken from a sick bird just this morning. Get to
know them well. They're no more than little specks, but all
the men who have studied chicken cholera believe that they
cause the disease."

He hurried on to say that, in 1869, an Alsatian veterinary
surgeon named Moritz had first noticed them in the corpses
of infected birds. He had called them "granulations." Nine
years later, Perroncito, an Italian veterinarian, had painstakingly made the first sketches of them. Another scientist,
Toussaint, after intense study, had demonstrated that they
were responsible for chicken cholera. Now Louis had as-
signed himself the task of ridding the world of the harm
done by them.

"To do that," he said, "we must first learn to grow these
little things so that we can study their every habit."

Roux and Chamberland remembered that statement with
a smile during the next weeks. Louis had made the goal
sound so simple to reach. It was anything but simple to

reach. Louis' notebook became pocked with the record of one failure after another.

"Today we tried Toussaint's idea of growing the cholera microbes in neutralized urine. In the beginning, all went well, but too soon the multiplication of the germs ceased."

And later:

"Two days ago we began sowing the little specks in yeast water. Results astonishing but discouraging. Within forty-eight hours, every microbe had disappeared!"

And still later:

"Weeks of continued failure. Is there no end to this work?"

Actually, as he wrote, the end was in sight, for, the next day, he began to experiment with a solution composed of chicken gristle neutralized with potash. A few hours after he had sterilized this broth at a temperature of one-hundred-and-ten to one-hundred-and-fifteen degrees centigrade, he felt Roux's hand on his shoulder and heard the boy's impulsive voice. "I think we've hit upon it this time, Professor. I'm sure we have!"

Louis' gesture of warning was automatic. A man of the laboratory should never speak too soon, not after so many experiments that had started out so beautifully had climaxed so miserably. He himself wasn't always able to live up to this creed, but at least he could caution the boy, "Not too fast. Not too fast. Time will tell."

But, deep inside himself, he felt a rising excitement. This broth *did* look encouraging. It was becoming cloudy, almost milky—always the sign of life within. He kept his voice calm, bracing himself against some unforeseen disappointment, as he told Émile, "Please put a drop of the culture on a slide."

One glance in the microscope told him the days of disappointment were past. Without taking his eye from the instrument, he signaled for a pen. Roux waved Chamberland to his side and they inclined their heads over the words that Louis scribbled in his notebook:

"Multitude of micro-organisms—multiplying rapidly— each narrow, almost strangled, at the middle—each no more than a speck—they hardly move—"

Louis brought his face up from the microscope. Dark hair fell across his forehead. His glasses sat crookedly on his nose. He was still trying, but now so unsuccessfully, to remain the dispassionate scientist. "I think you're right, Émile. I think we've hit upon it this time."

Work stopped at the other tables. Assistants crowded about Louis, all eager for a look in the microscope. The usually quiet room echoed with the sound of their voices. Even though most of the assistants had not participated in the experiment, they had felt the strain of the past weeks keenly. They had hoped and had been disappointed and had hoped again right along with their employer. Now they felt a part of the victory.

But, three mornings later, the lab was again silent—tensely silent—when Louis entered. Émile came quickly to him, his young face drawn, troubled. "Something's wrong with the broth, sir."

"What's happened?"

Louis didn't wait for a reply. He hurried to the flask containing the solution. He wanted to curse his leg. He never seemed able to move as quickly as he desired. The leg was always a leaden weight there below his left hip, dragging a little, slowing him.

He took up the flask. He held it to the window and saw

the distorted shapes of trees and buildings through the clear liquid. Yes, through the clear liquid! For more than seventy-two hours it had been cloudy with life. But now it was as transparent as water!

What had happened overnight in the flask? What strange trick had nature played? Had the germs died? Must he start all over again? He closed his mind to such questions as he transferred a drop of the fluid to a microscope stage.

A quick glance into the instrument and relief and amazement were flooding him all at once. The germs *weren't* dead, but somewhere in the dark, silent hours of the night nature *had* come to play her tricks on them!

Louis pulled Émile to the microscope. "Look at them, my boy! Nature has played the careless washerwoman. She has scrubbed them too hard and they have shrunk to less than half their size. They're so small we won't even be able to measure them. And don't ask me why they've become so tiny. I don't know. All I know is that we must see if they are vicious as ever."

Full upon him now was the work Louis abhorred in any experiment dealing with animals. Deliberately he must inject into defenseless creatures millions of venomous germs. The result was always sickness and suffering and death. Some called what he did cruel. Was it? He wondered. He hated to see the agony he induced. But out of such agony could come freedom from disease, a freedom that would find its way around the world. And so, like it or not, the job simply had to be done.

He placed mere drops of the solution on bread crumbs and fed them to chickens; within hours the animals were dead. Grains of feed that they pecked at and then could not swallow became the source of spreading the disease to other hens in the lab cages.

In his notebook, Louis wrote, "The animal suffering from this disease is powerless, staggering, its wings droop and its bristling feathers give it the shape of a ball; and irresistible somnolence overpowers it. If its eyes are made to open, it seems to awake from a deep sleep and death frequently supervenes after a dumb agony, before the animal has stirred from its place; sometimes there is a faint fluttering of wings for a few seconds."

Guinea pigs survived the injections much more successfully. They became ill, but, in a short while, were their scurrying, ever-sniffing selves again. Usually an abscess developed at the point of inoculation. Louis opened one such sore and found that it contained the microbes of cholera. They were imprisoned there as if in a test tube.

These were all interesting facts, each valuable in helping Louis understand the workings of the chicken cholera germ. But how could they help him cure or prevent the disease? He had to admit he did not know. He also did not know that he was soon to stumble quite accidentally on a method of prevention and that it was to be one of his most important discoveries.

The accident began on the day in 1879 when, finding he had no fresh solution available, he instructed Roux to inoculate several chickens with cholera microbes that were several weeks old. As usual, the birds promptly fell ill. There was no doubt in Louis' mind that the poor creatures would be dead by morning.

But next day they thoroughly confounded him by strutting about their cages in what appeared to be perfect health.

He stroked his beard and returned to stare at them all through the day. No ruffed up feathers. No drooping eyes. Not a sign of the fatal drowsiness. The birds *were* in perfect health.

"What's happened here?" he asked himself as many times as he returned to the cages. "Are they somehow immune to the disease? Were they always immune to it? Or are the old cholera germs weak?"

Though they were questions he definitely wanted to answer, he had no chance to seek the answers. He was leaving with Marie on their vacation that night. He dared not upset her by postponing their departure. He had done that sort of thing too many times in their life together.

The vacation lasted several weeks and, upon his return to the lab, Louis had quite forgotten the incident of the chickens who had refused to die. He planned to continue his regular series of inoculations and asked an attendant to fetch several chickens to him.

"I'm sorry, Professor," the attendant replied. "We have on hand only two new birds and the ones you inoculated just before your vacation."

Louis was thoughtful for a moment. "Oh, I remember. The ones that got well again."

"Yes."

"All right. Bring both lots to me."

He carried out the inoculations swiftly. Gently, all four birds were strapped to a work board, injected with a fresh solution, and returned to their cages. Louis, immersing himself in new ideas for his hydrophobia and anthrax studies, did not find the opportunity to visit the cages until the following morning.

What he saw upon arriving there sent him dashing to the door of the main laboratory, an excited cry bursting from his lips.

"Roux! Chamberland! Come here! Hurry!"

Vaccination

To Louis' right, Chamberland's face jumped up from a microscope. Directly ahead, Émile Roux bobbled a test tube, caught it, sighed with relief, and placed it in a rack. Louis saw the two young men exchange glances that clearly asked, "What's gone wrong now?" as they hurried to him.

Chamberland came through the door first and Louis caught his arm and pulled him to the nearest cage. Émile was no more than three steps behind, his narrow face ashen, bewildered.

Louis, hand arced toward the cage. "See these birds? I inoculated them yesterday. Quite dead, aren't they?"

Eyes completely round and mouths agape, the assistants looked, nodded and again exchanged glances that spoke so loudly in their silence, "Naturally, they're dead. What else was to be expected? Has the old man gone out of his head?"

Louis enjoyed the exchange immensely. No, he told himself, this old man hasn't lost his senses. He has just stumbled onto something so electrifying, so wonderful, that he cannot help but dramatize the moment.

He swung to the second cage, his hand outstretched, palm up, fingers taut. Here was what had so astounded him. Here were two very-much-alive chickens, clucking and pecking at the cage floor, pausing now and again to turn inquisitive yellow eyes on their visitors, particularly that noisy one with the waving arms. "And these fellows," Louis announced. "They, too, were inoculated yesterday!"

He wanted to laugh aloud. The expressions of his assistants fell apart, like porcelain vases shattering on the floor. Bewilderment became surprise, surprise became amazement, and amazement sheer confusion.

From their lips tumbled the very questions he had been asking himself these past minutes. What had happened? Why weren't the chickens dead? Did they have some mysterious resistance to cholera? Had the solution been prepared correctly?

He signaled for quiet. He tried to steady his trembling voice. "Now, listen carefully. The answer is astonishing, but, I think, very simple." He patted the second cage. "Some time ago, I had you, Émile, inoculate these birds for the first time with a solution that had been left standing in the lab several weeks. It made them only slightly ill and they recovered easily. Apparently, *the chicken cholera germs lose their strength when they get old.*"

"But why?" Émile asked. "What causes them to weaken with age?"

"I don't know. But, remember, the solution had been left standing in the air. Perhaps the oxygen in the atmosphere had something to do with it."

He continued to pat the cage, almost lovingly. "Yesterday, I inoculated them again, this time with a new and very strong solution—and they have remained perfectly well." He stepped to Roux and Chamberland, his eyes shining. "Do you see the significance of this? An animal can be made slightly ill with cholera germs weakened by age. When it recovers, it is *immune* from the disease. As did our lively chickens here, it can withstand the strongest cholera bugs we can find!"

He lifted his hands to their shoulders and shook them with a gentle roughness. "My friends, we are the most fortunate men in Europe. Blindly, quite by accident, we've made a remarkable discovery. We've stumbled upon a *protective vaccine*—the cholera germs themselves! The weakened germs enable the animal to fight off their more powerful brothers. They are traitors to their own kind." (In later years, science was to find that a vaccine causes the body to form "antibodies" which protect it from the disease in question.)

"It's a marvelous idea," Chamberland said. "But I'm afraid I see a difficulty right off—"

"I know," Louis interrupted. "How long must the cholera germs age before they are weak enough not to do the chickens any real harm?"

Chamberland nodded and Louis laughed. It was a very young laugh and sounded strange coming from behind a gray-streaked beard. Even the deep lines in his cheeks and the dark smudges below his eyes could not keep the look of youth out of his face. "My boy, that is a question the three of us are going to answer, even if it takes us years to do so!"

The search for the answer did not require years; in fact, it was completed in little more than three months. But it did require the greatest of patience. First, a large quantity of solution had to be prepared and poured into flasks. The neck of each flask was loosely plugged with a wad of cotton to allow air to enter slowly. Then the flasks were set aside to age for varying periods of time.

Louis tried to busy himself with other tasks while the aging process took place, but without success. He kept returning to the flasks to peer at them and snort angrily at how slowly time passed. He put his feelings into words for Marie. "I just might have within my grasp a boon to all mankind. The chicken cholera vaccine might lead to other vaccines—vaccines, my dear, that would protect from disease not only animals but human beings. Is it not a thought that makes you weak all over? I would give anything to be able to whip the sluggish minutes and hours to greater speed!"

Within three days, he opened the first flask and inoculated ten hens. Sickness and death followed. A week later another flask was unplugged and syringes filled. Again sickness and death. By the end of the month, he was beginning to see results.

He excitedly scribbled in his notebook, "Several days ago, all ten chickens became ill, as usual. But two did not die. When they had recovered, we inoculated them with a very strong solution. They remained perfectly well. They are immune. This is our first real progress."

Days later, he added, "The end is in sight. Death rate is cut in half. Only five birds dead out of ten from our latest inoculation. Five survivors immune."

The number of fatalities decreased and the degree of illness lessened steadily as the third month drew to a close. At last, there were no deaths and, shortly thereafter, the cholera germs were so old and so weak that they caused hardly a trace of disease at all.

"We've done it. We've done it!" Louis told his assistants early in 1880. "All the birds live. All of them became but slightly ill. And all of them remain healthy when they receive more than their share of deadly germs. We've found our vaccine!"

Roux and Chamberland smiled at the old man's happiness and Chamberland asked, "What are you going to call this process for protecting the chickens?"

"I've thought of that often," Louis said. "I think 'vaccination' is the only word for it."

"Of course," Chamberland answered. "I should have known. Vaccination. After Jenner."

"Yes."

The three men fell silent, each recalling the first time he had heard the stirring legend of Edward Jenner. Because of this humble, obscure Scottish physician, vaccination had long been practiced with the smallpox disease. Almost ninety years previously, in 1796 to be exact, Jenner had introduced into a scratch on the arm of a small boy some matter taken from the sore on the arm of a dairy maid who had contracted smallpox from a cow. This was the world's first vaccination, the word itself coming from *vacca,* meaning cow. Afterward, Jenner found that the boy did not take smallpox, even when the germs were introduced into his body.

"For all these years, no one has really known *why* the boy had been protected," Chamberland said. "But now we've found that weakened germs—attenuated germs—are the answer."

"Yes, we know they're the answer," Louis said jubilantly.

"And now the world must know of them. I know I've said it before, but it must be said again and again so everyone will hear: they're giants. Invisible giants, working everywhere for good and evil. In animals! In plants! In man!"

He rubbed his hands together in anticipation. He would tell the world of this latest news of the giants through the Academy of Medicine. It would be a magnificent moment for him. Not only would farmers in every land learn they were now free from a costly disease, but he would even the score with certain members of the Academy for the insulting things they had said about the importance of the giants in childbirth fever. They wouldn't like it—these pompous doctors—but they would have to admit the little germs could do great work in the world. And they would have to confess that this Pasteur knew what he was talking about when it came to disease, even if he was but a mere chemist.

When he limped to the platform at the Academy a short time later he was certain his chicken cholera report would earn loud applause. But, as he spoke, he became aware his listeners were not reacting as he had anticipated. True, here and there, a scientist leaned forward with interest. But most of the men managed to look downright bored! His heart was hammering hard and his face was crimson with anger when he concluded his report. A few had snickered during his final paragraphs. And one had had the audacity to bring out his watch and stare meaningfully at it.

He glared at the audience in the silence that followed his remarks, a silence that was broken for but a moment by a smattering of applause. Weak applause, indeed, in comparison to what he had expected! He wanted to call these well-dressed men fools. He knew they had not taken his words seriously because he was not a physician and because they seemed to hate new ideas. Couldn't they understand that, even though he was not a doctor, he was still a man of science? And couldn't they understand how stupid it was to fight against new truths, to call them worthless just because they were new?

He saw a bent figure rise from an aisle chair. It was Jules Guerin, white-haired and in his eighties. The old man leaned on a cane and his voice, addressing the assemblage with heavy sarcasm, came up to Louis.

"So Monsieur Pasteur has discovered the reason why vaccines work? Monsieur Pasteur is very famous. But he wants to be more famous. He wants to be greater than Jenner. Well, he should stop trying and leave medicine to doctors!"

"You know as well as I," Louis shouted, the force of his words carrying him down to the aisle, directly to Guerin, "that much can be done for medicine in the laboratories of chemists, biologists, physicists—"

Guerin fixed narrow, red-rimmed eyes on him. "I do not, Monsieur! I only know at this moment," he cried, his mocking gaze circling the room, "that I am thoroughly bored by all this nonsensical fussing with mere chickens!"

A roar of laughter greeted the words. Guerin bowed to the crowd. Louis felt his anger turn to cold fury. They had no right to smear his work with ridicule. Couldn't they see that chickens—comical little things that they were—were as important as life and death to thousands of farmers, that these small animals meant the difference between starvation and well-being to families all over the world? And couldn't these brilliant, scornful doctors realize that his work could lead to vaccines that could shield men and women and children from death?

The blood was pounding so hard in his ears that he could barely hear Guerin's next words. "Fuss all you like with your precious hens, Monsieur! But how dare you waste the time of doctors with them! We have more important matters to consider!"

Now his own voice was dim in his ears and it was shouting, "And how dare you mock a scientific discovery after some of your ridiculous experiments?"

Guerin's head snapped back as if he had been slapped. His hair seemed to stand right on end. He pounded the floor with his cane. "Just what do you mean—ridiculous?"

Louis told him exactly what he meant. He sarcastically outlined a number of Guerin's laboratory failures. He did so with such accuracy that the audience could not keep from bursting into laughter. Guerin stared at him, his mouth working savagely. Suddenly his cane shot off the floor. The old doctor stumbled forward, a white-knuckled, bony hand waving the stick above his head and preparing to bring it down on this insolent Pasteur. Louis' hands snatched at Guerin's wrists. He would have caught them and he would have struggled with this aged opponent, perhaps tumbling to the carpeted floor, had not doctors—no longer laughing but now shouting—jumped between them and pulled them away from each other.

The room was still in a turmoil when Louis stomped out of the Academy. Behind him, someone was searching for a glass of water for Guerin and crying that the white-haired physician was certain to suffer a heart attack. Louis knew the people on the street thought him mad. He had pulled his hat right down to his ears. His tie was crooked, his coat open, and his waistcoat rumpled. His face was a flaming red and he couldn't stop muttering to himself. Let these strangers think what they wanted about him. He didn't care. Not a jot! His great day had been ruined. His greatest scientific discovery to date had been soiled by ridicule. He had been made to look a fool.

"We *both* must have looked like fools," he told Marie that night when he had sufficiently calmed himself to manage a sheepish smile. "Guerin is as skinny as the handle of a spoon and I'm a half-cripple and almost sixty. What a sight we must have made, ready to battle it out to the end."

"Well," Marie said soothingly, "my advice is to forget the whole affair."

Guerin, however, would not let him forget it. Friends of the old physician called at the lab next day to present his challenge to a duel. Louis, a Catholic, had no choice but to refuse.

He made an effort to put the incident in the past by formally apologizing to the Academy and remarking that men of science should forget personal differences and work together.

For days following the apology, he was the most silent of men. He went about his daily tasks with a frown. His whole manner seemed preoccupied, distant.

"It's a shame," Roux told Chamberland. "This thing with Guerin has completely destroyed the joy of his new discovery."

Chamberland glanced to where Louis sat at a microscope. "Well, he'll have to get over it sooner or later."

Actually, the incident, though the memory of it still stung, was not responsible for Louis' preoccupation. It was his churning imagination that drove him to silence, that plagued him with two constantly repeated questions.

"Can the secret of the chicken cholera vaccine now be applied to other vaccines for animals and men? Can it help us find a vaccine against the dread disease, anthrax, which we've been studying so long?"

He felt the answer to both questions was "Yes."

So, he told himself, forget Guerin. Forget you've been humiliated and your discovery scorned. Forget all these things and get down to work.

It was very easy to say, "Let's produce an anthrax vaccine."

It was quite another matter actually to develop such a vaccine, for a problem cropped up immediately that made the task almost impossible.

The germs of chicken cholera had weakened with age. But not so the anthrax rods. As they aged, they produced the spores in ever increasing quantities. And the spores were the fellows who gave Louis all the trouble. They were vicious and deadly, and they stubbornly sidestepped his every effort to reduce their strength.

Charles Chamberland summed up their toughness one afternoon in the lab. "After eight or ten years, spores found in the graves of anthrax victims are still as strong as ever. As long as they're around, we'll not have our vaccine."

"I agree," Louis said. "So there is but one way we can proceed. If the spores are too powerful for us after they're born, then we must keep them from being born in the first place. Without the spores, the rods will weaken nicely with age."

Those few words launched them on experiments that lasted for weeks. As usual, Louis drove his men hard. They worked long and exhausting hours. Their eyes became bleary and their backs ached from continually bending over the solutions in which they hoped the rods would grow without producing spores. Sometimes they even slept at the lab, and, at other times, Louis was more than reluctant to allow them to go out for a breath of air.

All the hardship and toil were rewarded in a few weeks. Louis and his assistants, after countless failures, finally succeeded in growing anthrax rods that were incapable of developing spores. This was done by placing the rods in a neutralized chicken broth at a temperature of forty-two or forty-three degrees centigrade.

Louis was triumphant. "We've cornered our little bug. We've taken his spores away from him and have made him quite defenseless. Now he'll cooperate with us when we try to weaken him."

Allowing cultures of the rods to weaken and age in air, the three scientists noted the same phenomena they had seen in the chicken cholera germs. Chamberland wrote in his notebook, "After eight days, for instance, our culture which originally killed ten sheep out of ten, only kills four or five; after twelve days it does not kill any; it merely communicates to animals a benignant malady which preserves them from the deadly form."

True to Chamberland's words, Louis had inoculated many sheep with the weakened virus. They became but slightly ill. Then, after injecting into them deadly strains of anthrax bugs, Louis was delighted to find the animals immune to the strongest attacks of the disease.

The results prompted him to declare, "Now we have a vaccine that can be sent to all parts of the world."

Roux and Chamberland cautioned him not to speak too quickly. Their work had produced a good vaccine for sheep. But their attempts to develop a vaccine for cattle had not yet met with success. Much work remained to be done on this latter vaccine before it could be considered usable.

But Louis was deaf to their warnings. Another proof of the power of micro-organisms in the world had been found, and, as usual, he could not remain silent. He hurried to the Academy of Sciences—having discontinued his visits to the Academy of Medicine since the Guerin travesty—and outlined the vaccine in detail. He concluded his report with the glowing prophecy that the day was close at hand when all animals would be free of the terror of anthrax.

His announcement of the new vaccine excited and divided all France. It was the same old story for Louis. Many scientists and farmers thought his discovery magnificent, particularly the farmers who saw in it the end of a costly disease. Others, especially medical men and veterinary surgeons, felt he was again invading fields about which he knew nothing. One such man was Monsieur Rossignol, editor of *The Veterinary Journal*.

The word "microbe" had just been invented by a Dr. Sedillot as a name for all microscopic life, and Rossignol angrily wrote in his paper:

Will you have some microbe? It is everywhere present. Microbiolatry is the fashion; it reigns undisputed; it is a doctrine which defies discussion, especially when its Pontiff, the learned M. Pasteur, has pronounced the sacramental words, "I have spoken." Alone the microbe is and shall be the characteristic of disease; that is understood and taken for granted; from now on the germ theory shall be exalted above pure clinics; for only the Microbe is true, and Pasteur is its prophet.

A printed attack on Louis wasn't enough for Rossingnol. The editor drummed his desk top and racked his brain for some way to silence the much-too-active tongue of this Pasteur for all time to come; some way that would make it impossible for him ever to stick his blunt nose into medical affairs again. A simple but, so Rossingnol felt, highly effective plan fell into mind. Why not challenge Pasteur to a public demonstration of his magical vaccine? The attention of the world would be focused on such a demonstration. Pasteur's vaccine would fail, of course. Pasteur would earn nothing but derision. He would reveal himself to be no more than a talkative fool. He would be forced to hide his face forever behind the locked doors of his lab.

Rossingnol immediately went to work on his scheme. He collected money to stage the demonstration. He approached the Agricultural Society of Melun and told them, with a very straight face, that the world was entitled to see what Professor Pasteur had accomplished. The Society gave their endorsement to the demonstration and agreed to make space available for it.

Thus it was that one afternoon Baron de la Rochette, a gentleman farmer and Chairman of the Society, called on Louis at the École Normale lab. He was tall and gray-haired and well dressed, and he looked completely out of place among all the test tubes as he quietly presented Rossingnol's challenge to the scientist.

"The demonstration will take place at the Pouilly-le-Fort farm, just outside Melun. You will inoculate one group of animals with your vaccine. A second group of animals will go without vaccination. Then *all* the animals will be injected with a deadly form of anthrax microbes. If the vaccinated animals remain healthy while the others fall sick, you will have shown the world the true value of your vaccine."

Roux and Chamberland had departed from Paris on a well-earned vacation the day before, but many another assistant overheard the presentation of the challenge. They exchanged nervous, almost frightened, glances. It was too soon for any sort of public demonstration. Much more work needed to be done on the vaccine. Surely, Pasteur would not accept the challenge.

Aghast, they heard Louis say with his usual confidence:

"I shall be most happy to appear at Pouilly-le-Fort on whatever date you stipulate."

The assistants nearby groaned.

Oh, if Roux and Chamberland were only here! Perhaps they could have kept the old man from speaking those impetuous words.

Perhaps they could have convinced him that this whole affair seemed to be nothing more than a giant trap!

CHAPTER 14

The Pouilly-le-Fort

Experiment

As soon as Baron de la Rochette departed, Louis hurried a telegram off to vacationing Roux and Chamberland. "Return to Paris immediately," he instructed. His excitement was burned into every word. "Opportunity at hand to show world effectiveness of anthrax vaccines!"

Less than forty-eight hours later, the not-at-all rested assistants again stood in the lab. They hadn't even dared go home first and their luggage was strewn about their feet as they heard Louis describe the challenge and chortle:

"Just think of it! With the greatest scientists in France looking on, we're going to vaccinate on several occasions a large group of sheep and cattle. Another group of like animals will be left without inoculation."

He was much too jubilant to pay any heed to young eyebrows that suddenly dipped in troubled frowns. "Then, some weeks later, we will inject *all* the animals with the most deadly anthrax bacilli we can grow!" Now Roux and Chamberland were shifting nervously from foot to foot. Very nervously. Still, he gave their actions and expressions no attention. His voice was the voice of a prophet who clearly sees every single moment of the future. "And the whole world will learn what we have learned. The vaccinated animals will remain perfectly healthy. But the ones not vaccinated—each and every one of them will die within two short days."

He glared triumphantly from one young face to the other. "My boys, it is the opportunity of a lifetime! It is . . ."

Abruptly, his voice faded. Something was wrong. There were no smiles flashing back at his own smile. There was no enthusiasm to match his own. There was no talk of getting right down to work. There was only—only—what was it? Hesitation? Nervousness?

His tone was brittle.

"Well, what's the matter?"

Roux was the first to answer. He gestured apologetically. "Professor, have you thought this might be a wrong move? The work is very delicate. As fine as this lab is, our facilities are still primitive. We might produce inferior vaccines at the very moment when perfect ones are vital. We might not protect the animals at all!"

"Nonsense," Louis said.

"Sir, listen to reason," Chamberland pleaded. "Our methods for producing the vaccines are far from perfect. Either of two things may happen if we produce a bad lot of vaccines. If they're too strong, they'll kill the inoculated animals; if they're too weak or if we accidentally kill the rods, they won't protect the animals against the strong doses of anthrax bugs."

"And there's another thing," Roux said. "Our vaccine for sheep works fine. But what about the vaccine for cows? It's far from being really developed. It might not work at all."

"If any of the things happen that we've mentioned," Chamberland said, "you'll be the laughing stock of all France. You'll give your enemies that very tool they need to smash your reputation!"

"No, no!" Louis cried. "We must go through with it. We'll produce good vaccines. The cow vaccine will work. A chance like this to attract world attention to the power of microbes may never come again. And we won't fail. I *know* we won't!"

The assistants shrugged helplessly. The old man's mind couldn't—and woudn't—be changed. He was ready to stake his entire reputation on a single experiment, more than ready to do so because the world simply had to know of the invisible giants, that indeed they were giants and important to all, even the tiniest of infants. All right. There was but one thing to do—join him. Work with him. Trust him. Labor to obtain perfect vaccines. Give him every ounce of your support and strength. Glory with him in triumph. Or stand by him loyally in failure.

The date for the test was fixed at May 5, 1881. Not a single major French newspaper failed during April to devote hundreds of words to the experiment. The French public learned that twenty-five of the sheep donated by the Melun Agricultural Society were to be vaccinated once, then a second time twelve to fifteen days later; that ten cows belonging to Baron de la Rochette would be inoculated; that twenty-five sheep and four cows would not receive Pasteur's new and almost magical solution; that, finally, both lots of animals would be given heavy doses of the anthrax bugs.

Time and again, Louis came to Roux and Chamberland to show them long columns of black print as they painstakingly cooked and bottled for aging the anthrax solutions to be used at Melun.

"Look at this! All France knows what we're doing! Everyone reads and talks of the little germs." He bent low and peered at the bottles and slapped his knee with the newspaper and called to the millions of little beings he could not see, "Hear that? You're becoming very famous!"

Roux and Chamberland shuddered at his childlike glee. "Yes," each was thinking, "everyone reads and talks of the little germs. But soon everyone may read and talk of a dismal failure. What will happen to the glee then? What will happen to the spirit and the genius that reside within that small, bent body?"

Louis would have shuddered, too, had he known Rossignol was devouring the newspaper reports as eagerly as he and congratulating himself for contriving such a fine trick to tear down from his pedestal of greatness that mighty, know-it-all, talkative, scientific magician, Pasteur.

At the beginning of May, Louis and his assistants carried the phials of weakened anthrax bacilli by train to Melun to complete arrangements for the test. They rode out to Pouilly-le-Fort on the morning of the fifth.

They found the road running past the farm jammed with carriages and horses. Spectators—hundreds of them—were hurrying through the front gates and jostling each other for places in the large circle that was forming at the center of the farmyard. The swiftness of their movements and the rattle of their voices and their laughter gave the place a circus air.

Roux clapped a hand to his forehead. He groaned, "Everyone in the world is here!"

Chamberland shot a hard glance at him. It clearly warned: "Watch your tone. Don't say anything to upset the old man now!"

But Chamberland felt his heart sink, too. Present were Senators of the Republic, scientists, physicians, veterinary surgeons, newspaper correspondents, and countless farmers. A failure under any circumstances would be terrible, but a failure in front of all these men . . .

His eyes went to Louis. Could this pale-faced man live through such a thing? Even though he had been filled with vitality these past weeks, the scientist looked much too haggard, much too tired. His eyes were webbed with tiny red veins. The lines beneath his colorless cheeks looked like deep knife scars. His beard was almost white. Suddenly the boy wanted to throw an arm about this beloved, fragile master and somehow pour some of his own strength into the little man.

But Louis needed no support. He limped to the center of the circle. He heard a smattering of applause and, here and there, a cheer. He saw some of these grand men nudge each other, their lips upturned at the corners, ready to snicker. He saw others staring at him with mere curiosity, as though he were some sort of freak. Still others, the reporters, raised pencils to note pads. So! Some were on his side—the farmers who hoped so desperately that anthrax would disappear from their lives. Others hoped he would fail; they were the veterinarians, annoyed because he had the audacity to stick his nose into their work, jealous because he had done what they could not do. And the rest had come to see a show or had come because they had been told to do so. Fine! Excellent! He would show the whole lot of them. Let some of them snicker now. They would cheer him before he was done with them.

Roux and Chamberland crouched near him and unpacked their Pravaz syringes. Louis ordered the animals to be vaccinated to be brought from the barn. Out into the sunlight came the long line of beasts, each held by two farmers, each frightened of the circle of spectators that now tightened and fell silent.

He glanced down at Roux. The boy's face was dead white.

"Keep a clear head and a steady hand," he cautioned softly. Somewhere deep inside him a chill trembling was starting. He forced a smile. "Everything is going to be fine. Just fine."

He stepped back and watched, silent and motionless, as the first of the animals, a bleating, nervous sheep, was brought to a halt before Roux. The chill trembling turned ice cold within him. Now that the very moment of the trial was at hand, he felt his courage desert him. Full upon him was the realization that his whole career was in danger. Émile and Charles had been right. He should never have gone through with this thing. Poorly prepared vaccines might kill the animals or fail to protect them; and he really didn't have the cow vaccine developed to the point of absolute safety. Oh, I've been a fool, he told himself. A complete fool! Well, it was too late to retreat now.

He saw that Émile had finished vaccinating the sheep.

The cows were brought to Roux. The boy stood up. Perspiration beaded his forehead. Louis saw his eyes swing to him and he saw in them the unvoiced cry:

"We've gone far enough, Professor. We've taken enough chances. Call this thing to a halt. The cattle vaccine. It can't be trusted."

Louis returned his gaze with all the steadiness he could muster. He wanted to do exactly what Roux's eyes were asking him to do—flee from this field of battle. But he had no choice but to say:

"Continue the injections, Émile."

There was no mistaking the command in his voice.

The boy nodded, took a deep breath and plunged the needle into the thick hide just behind the shoulder of the first cow. For one so frightened, his hand was astonishingly steady.

Within five minutes, his job was done.

One last formality remained. Each vaccinated sheep was given a distinguishing mark on one ear, each cow on a horn. Then began the days of waiting. If just one beast became ill from the five drops of protective solution he had received, the whole experiment would be branded a failure at the very beginning. Just one. That's all that was required. Louis returned to Paris and, daily, waited in an agony of suspense for his assistants to report temperature readings from Pouilly-le-Fort. It seemed to him his first easy breath of each day was drawn the very second he learned that not one animal was suffering an abnormal rise in temperature.

The second vaccination took place twelve days later, on May 17. A stronger vaccine was used. Again a large crowd was present, made up mostly of veterinary surgeons. But this time, Louis noted, the snickering had all but vanished. He had passed the first obstacle in the test. His vaccines had not made the animals sick, and the cattle vaccine seemed to be working properly. He could see the beginnings of awe in the eyes of these men who were his severest critics. He knew the questions they were asking themselves. Was this man Pasteur right after all? Had he really found the giant spade with which to dig an ocean-deep moat between animals and anthrax?

More waiting, more temperature readings and, at last, the day of the final test was at hand, the last day of May, when both vaccinated and unvaccinated animals would have the most deadly anthrax bugs Louis could find thrust beneath their hides.

Hundreds of people had been at Pouilly-le-Fort at the beginning of the month. Now Louis was certain that thousands jammed the huge farmyard. The sight of them chilled him. He knew that some of them had drunk to his failure earlier that morning. All were silent. Every eye was on him, following intently his slow, limping progress to the pen behind the barn.

He checked the unvaccinated animals. Poor unsuspecting creatures. They would be dead within forty-eight hours. But what about the vaccinated lot over here? What if the vaccines used earlier in the month hadn't worked properly, hadn't been prepared correctly. Then they, too, would die. And his career would be at an end.

He turned quickly from the thought and returned to the center of the yard. Roux had unpacked the glass syringes filled with their deadly poison.

"Are you ready?"

Émile swallowed hard. In his mind were the very same thoughts Louis had been thinking. His reply, "Yes," sounded like the gasp of a suffocating man.

Louis spoke tersely to the farmer at his side.

"Bring out the animals—both lots."

His voice carried to the inner rim of the silent circle. A scraping sound came to him from all sides as the crowd pushed forward several steps. He glimpsed faces turning swiftly from one to another and heard his words repeated a hundred different ways:

"It's going to begin now—"

"They're bringing the animals out—"

"It's starting—"

"Here they come—"

Again he was motionless, his eyes narrow and hard on Émile's hand as it sent the anthrax bugs scattering into the tissues beneath the thick hides of the unvaccinated sheep and cows. Next came the vaccinated animals; into their hides went the bugs that had but one mission in life—to kill. But these animals had to live! They had to remain healthy, protected against the poison of the bugs. The vaccines had to prove successful.

Now he could think and pray no longer. Both groups of animals had been inoculated and a haggard Émile Roux was approaching him. Forty-eight hours would tell the story. Would he be hero? Would he be fool?

Émile wiped a sleeve across his damp forehead.

"Well, Professor, the hardest part is done."

Louis shook his head and managed a wry smile. "No, my boy, the worst is yet to come—living with ourselves if we have failed."

The second day of June at two o'clock in the afternoon. That was the moment, he said, when next he would set eyes on the animals. It was two days away; he had to live out forty-eight hours of aimlessly roaming the lab, of staring at his assistants without really seeing them, of trying to push from his mind the knowledge that he faced ruin and ridicule if but one vaccinated animal now sickened and died. Madame Pasteur tried to comfort him, but to no avail, even though the reports from Pouilly-le-Fort were heartening. The unvaccinated animals had become ill. Their condition worsened steadily. The previously vaccinated lot remained quite well.

But would they still be well on that second day of June at two in the afternoon?

Or, in some hour before that time, would they suddenly become ill and perish?

Those were the terrifying questions that made sleep and all other work impossible.

Thursday, June 2, arrived. Louis traveled to Melun, but refused to go on to Pouilly-le-Fort until the exact hour he had specified.

When at last he did ride out to the farm, he found its grounds lost from view beneath a surging tide of humanity. The greatest dignitaries in France were present. In fact, it seemed to Louis that all France was crowding about his carriage. The great crowd fell silent when he stepped to the ground.

Why are they suddenly so quiet, he asked himself.

Fear crowded his heart.

Was it because they pitied him because they knew what he did not yet know—that he had failed?

He must get to the animal pen immediately.

He stepped forward and the crowd parted before him. A Senator bowed to him. A veterinary surgeon lifted his silk hat.

Were these gestures of respect or scorn?

He would know in scant minutes.

The walk to the pen seemed interminable. Louis wanted to run. But that was impossible. Such a thing couldn't be done in front of these men and his left leg would never stand it. So you must walk slowly and be patient. Every limping step brings you a bit closer. Ah, now your hands are on the gate.

He pushed the gate open and stepped into the pen. Carefully, deliberately, he ran his eyes over the animals.

His legs turned to water.

Relief flooded him.

The vaccinated animals were alive, each and every one of them healthy and stumbling about in fear of the great crowd. But those poor brutes who had received the deadly bugs without previous vaccination—they were dead. All but two. And these pitiful things were on their sides, glassy-eyed in the last stages of anthrax.

Tears filled his eyes. He groped his way back to the open gate. He faced the crowd. He could hardly see them. His voice refused to be more than a whisper.

"It is a success."

Yes, it was a success! The grandest success in the world! The vaccines had all been prepared correctly! The cattle vaccine had worked! All danger was past.

For a moment, the intense silence lingered in the farmyard. Then it was shattered by a tumultuous roar. Silk hats were flung into the air. Usually reserved and very dignified gentlemen grasped each other and grabbed at Louis' hand. Words of congratulation struck his ears from every direction. Senators, farmers, doctors, merchants, veterinarians, and reporters passed before his eyes. Even Rossingnol, who had plotted his downfall, was there. This man who now knew how wrong he had been to attack Pasteur elbowed his way through the crowd and gripped the scientist's shoulders and cried again and again, "A stunning success, Professor! A stunning success!"

Now Roux and Chamberland reached him and positioned themselves at his elbows. Slowly, gently, they led him through the jostling, frenzied crowd to the shelter of the carriage.

He fell back against the cushions. Tears had reached his beard. He had lived so many fine moments, but this was the greatest of all! The boys were bending over him eagerly, happily, pressing their own congratulations on him. He wanted to thank them for their support, their endless hours of toil, their patience with his long silences during the dark moments of stress.

He tried to speak. Nothing emerged but a quiet laugh and the simple confession:

"I'm so very tired."

Hydrophobia

Hydrophobia.

What terror that one word held for the world of the 1880's.

Fearful parents knew it to be a merciless killer, caused by the gnashing teeth of a dog or wolf mad with rabies. The death it brought was a horrible, choking thing. Victims were possessed by a raging fever, overpowered by a thirst they could not satisfy because they had lost the power to swallow. They found sleep impossible and tossed in agony, their jaws snapping uncontrollably, until they slipped into a final coma. It was a disease that left no survivors.

In 1884, Louis was deep in his study of this killer. He was sixty-two years old, and three years of tribute had passed since the Pouilly-le-Fort experiment. He had won from the French government the Grand Cross of the Legion of Honor for his chicken cholera and anthrax vaccines. It was an award he had refused to accept until the government agreed to present Roux and Chamberland with the Red Ribbon.

The year 1882 saw him claim his finest honor to date—his election to the Académie Française, a group composed of France's most distinguished leaders in the arts and sciences. Ernest Renan, President of the Académie, welcomed him with words that were to ring down through the years. After commenting that the Académie could not pass judgment on his scientific achievements, Renan observed that there was something in Louis that all the members *could* recognize: "This common basis for all beautiful and true work, this divine flame, this indefinable spirit, which inspires science, literature and art, we have found in you, Sir—it is genius. No one has traversed with so sure a step the regions of elemental nature; your scientific life is like a luminous track across the great night of the infinitely small, in the last abysses of being in which life is born."

Work and tragedy also wove themselves into the fabric of Louis' life during these years. He studied cattle pleuropneumonia and developed a vaccine for swine erysipelas. He dispatched a commission of young scientists to Alexandria to fight a cholera epidemic. The epidemic claimed the life of one of his most beloved assistants, twenty-six-year-old Louis Thullier.

All honors, grief, and past work were forgotten one morning in 1884 when Louis, with Roux and Chamberland at his shoulder, stood in the lab and watched the approach of two attendants. Louis could not help but think the attendants the most courageous of men that morning, for lashed between them by means of rope was a rabid bulldog. The animal's hoarse growling echoed round the walls. His eyes rolled, greenish foam clouded his mouth, and he snapped viciously at the gloved hands that lifted him to a work table and then held his great head motionless.

Louis stepped to that massive head. Behind him, Roux and Chamberland stopped breathing. He put a thin glass tube to his lips and, quite deliberately, lowered his face to within inches of the animal's dripping lips. The dog snarled at him and tried to fling itself at his face. Carefully and with agonizing slowness, Louis moved the tube to the greenish foam and drew a portion of the stuff up into it. Then he straightened and heard Roux and Chamberland start to breathe again. The dog was quickly returned to his cage. Louis passed the tube to Émile without speaking. Words were unnecessary. The boy knew exactly what to do, so often had this experiment been performed.

The deadly saliva was inserted into a syringe and several pigs were inoculated with it. The results of the inoculations were visible the following morning.

"Everyone of the pigs became ill with hydrophobia and died during the night," Louis said. "It is the same as always."

"Yes. The same as always," Émile repeated. The assistant was frowning. Louis detected in his voice a note of disgust. It was easy to guess what was in his mind.

"Go ahead," Louis prompted gently. "Say what you think —that the experiment has shown us nothing new; that we're as far from wiping out hydrophobia as we were five years ago."

Émile's somber eyes met his quarely. "Well, it's true, Professor," he said, almost testily. "What do you know about this disease that we didn't know when Doctor Bourrel first interested you in it? Nothing at all." He began to tick off his points on his fingers. "All we know is that the disease is carried to humans in the saliva of rabid dogs. And that it takes a different length of time to strike each of its victims; some people fall ill within days; others in two weeks; some remain well for months. And—"

"And, worst of all, we don't even know what the hydrophobia germ looks like," Louis said. "That's what you were going to say next, right? We've examined hundreds of dogs and patients. We've seen all sorts of germs in them, but we've never been able to point to one of those germs and say with absolute certainty, 'You're the one. You're the one we're after.'"

Émile gestured helplessly. "Yes. How can we fight a germ we can't see? For all we know, we may never find a cure. The world may have to go on using the method of cauterizing wounds to ward off hydrophobia."

Louis flinched, as he always did when cauterizing was mentioned. Sharp and terrible in his mind was a boyhood memory. When he had been but nine, a mad wolf had come down the streets of Arbois and had attacked eight people. Seven of the poor souls had contracted hydrophobia and died. Only one, a little friend of his called Nicolle, had been spared the disease because her wounds had been cauterized with a hot iron. Louis had seen her treated in the smithy's shop. He could still hear her screams this very day. He asked quietly, "Do you wish to abandon the study, Émile?"

The boy shook his head. A deep crimson stain came up into his face. He regretted his show of disappointment. "Oh, no, sir. It's just that I wish we could find a way to uncover some new facts."

Louis swung his eyes to Chamberland. "And you, Charles, do you wish to quit?"

"Of course not. But I feel exactly as Émile does. I'd give a month's pay to find something new."

"And I, too," Louis said. He leaned back in his chair and fingered his beard thoughtfully. An idea had been hovering at the back of his mind for weeks. Perhaps now was the time to speak of it. He decided it was and said, "You say our studies have shown us nothing new. I think you're wrong. We've seen that hydrophobia doesn't take the same time to strike each of its victims, and we've seen how the patients—animals and humans alike—behave as the illness progresses. These are old facts, of course, but they have suggested something new to me, something that might enable us to actually see the hydrophobia bug at last. I think they have pointed to the place in the body where the bug finally comes to rest and does his greatest damage—*the victim's brain and nervous system.*"

He smiled inwardly. Émile's face, so despondent just a moment ago, was now alive with new interest. Charles' expression was amused; Louis well knew what he was thinking, "What will the old boy come up with next?"

The scientist pressed home his idea. "It would explain why the victims fall ill at different times. The germs must travel all the way from the place of the bite to the brain. They travel at different speeds. And sometimes they get lost or are overpowered by other forces in the body and never reach the brain, enabling a lucky few to avoid the disease altogether. Too, it would explain the convulsions the victims suffer when the disease is at hand." He regarded his assistants with what he knew must be a self-satisfied smile. "Do you think it an idea worth testing? Do you think we might look to the brain for our little germs?"

He would have been greatly disappointed had his questions received anything but the enthusiastic nods he saw.

A whole new series of experiments was designed and launched. The first of these was very simple. Some brain matter from dead rabid dogs was drawn up into a glass tube, placed in a vial heated to 200 degrees centigrade, mixed with sterilized broth or water and then injected into a large number of rabbits. All but a very few of the rabbits so inoculated contracted hydrophobia and died. Louis sighed with satisfaction. The experiment had been simple, yes, but effective. It had done its small part to prove his idea correct. The germs of hydrophobia had been present in the brains of the dead dogs.

Now a not-so-simple experiment was at hand—injecting rabid matter directly into a dog's brain to see how quickly, if at all, it took effect. The very thought of the experiment filled Louis with dread.

"I just can't do it," he told Roux. "It will involve trephining the dog—boring a small hole into his skull. It will be so painful and it's sure to leave him paralyzed."

Émile spoke to him as he might to a child. "Nothing of the sort will happen. The dog won't be paralyzed. And he won't be in pain. He'll be chloroformed. The whole operation shouldn't last more than just a few minutes."

Louis wouldn't be convinced. He was certain the animal would suffer. He fled from Émile and the thought of the operation with the words, "Perhaps another way can be found. I must have time to think."

But there was no other way. He knew it, and Émile and Chamberland knew it. Nevertheless, the entire hydrophobia project was stalled for several days while Louis wracked his brains uselessly. The delay chaffed at Émile's nerves and amused Charles.

"How is it?" Émile cried in exasperation to his fellow assistant one afternoon when Louis was out, "How is it, I ask you, that he can be so brilliant in many things and yet so utterly stupid about this operation? Any doctor will tell you it's painless."

"Every man has funny little gaps in his knowledge." Charles grinned. "Pasteur's not a medical doctor, so, very simply, he's never really gotten it into his head how painless surgery can be. It's strange but true."

"Strange is right!" Émile agreed vehemently. "He isn't afraid to give hundreds of animals the worst diseases on earth so that he can study them. And he isn't particularly fond of dogs. Yet this simple operation causes him to tremble in his boots."

Chamberland shrugged. "Just blame it on some little quirk in that magnificent mind of his. I can't explain it. All I know is that it's there and there's nothing we can do about it."

"But there's something we *can do* about the operation," Émile said. He had been perched on the edge of a work bench and now he dropped to the floor. "Where did Pasteur go this afternoon?"

"To an Académie meeting."

"Then he won't be back for quite some time."

"Not until tomorrow morning." Charles Chamberland stared closely at his friend's face. His grin widened, became positively devilish. "Are you going to do what I think you're going to do?"

"Yes. Are you with me?"

"Only if you actually know how to trephine a dog."

"I do. I've seen it done at the hospital a number of times."

"Then I'm with you all the way. Let's go."

The two young men hurried a dog from the animal room to a work table. They gently strapped him to an operating board and placed him under chloroform. A small circular disc was sawed out of his skull. Chamberland passed a minute portion of infected matter to Roux and the latter injected it directly into the exposed brain. Then he replaced the disc, washed the wound with carbolic, and stitched the skin back together again. The dog was carried back to his cage a few minutes after he had been taken from it.

When Louis discovered what his assistants had done, he rushed fearfully to the animal room, certain he would find the dog paralyzed or in great pain. Instead, he was greeted by a picture of perfect health; the dog bounded out of his cage and, with much barking and tail wagging, thrust his forepaws up to the scientist's waist. Roux and Chamberland, watching from the door, saw Louis drop to one knee, caress the animal and laugh at the wet nose that pressed itself against all parts of his face. The assistants exchanged satisfied grins. Pasteur's silly dread of trephining was fast dissolving before their very eyes.

The dog remained in fine health for fourteen days. Then all the characteristics of hydrophobia appeared—the hoarse growling, the greenish foam, the bloodshot eyes, the senseless lunging at anyone or anything in view. Death came within hours and Louis knew they had advanced another step in proving his idea.

More dogs were trephined. All of them sickened and died, and the third in the series of experiments was commenced. A portion of brain matter from one of these unfortunates was introduced into a rabbit. Upon his death, infected matter from his brain was injected into another rabbit and then another and another until more than one hundred rabbits had been so inoculated. The outcome raised Louis' spirits high. Victory was close at hand. He felt its presence in every fiber of his being, and he pointed an accusing finger at Roux.

"So you are the one who thought we'd never find anything new. Well, look at what the past experiment has shown us," he chortled. "As the hydrophobia bug passed from rabbit to rabbit it grew stronger until, by the final injection, the disease required but seven days to appear. We can now control the time it takes to strike. And, best of all, we have proved conclusively my idea that the bug finally locates itself in the brain. It is now time to turn that bug from a killer into a protective vaccine."

Émile admitted the value of the findings, but cautioned, "But we haven't accomplished what we set out to do. We still haven't seen the germ. How can we hope to manufacture a vaccine out of something that continues to remain hidden from view?"

"You're right. We've haven't seen the bug. But we know where he is. That's all that is important," Louis said. "Before now, we've weakened germs by exposing them to the air. Now we'll weaken this fellow by merely *exposing the place where he lives to the air*. That will do just fine!"

Accordingly, Louis removed the spinal cord from a diseased rabbit and suspended it in a sterile tube. Air of a temperature of twenty-three degrees centigrade was allowed to enter the tube through a plug of cotton wool. Once within the tube, it was kept dry by pieces of potash at the bottom of the vessel.

After fourteen days, a solution of the dried cord was injected into several healthy dogs. Next they received an injection of cord aged thirteen days, then one from a cord twelve days old. The inoculations continued daily until a final one was made from a cord dried the very same day. The dogs remained well over the two weeks required for the shots. Good. The germs had been properly weakened, Louis concluded. Then the dogs were exposed to the bites of rabid dogs and subjected to fatal doses of hydrophobia bugs.

Louis was beside himself with joy. He knew that, had he been younger, he would have danced right out of the lab, just as he had done years and years ago after he had solved Mitscherlich's riddle. But he was much too old for such cavortings now. All he could do was strike the work table to emphasize his words to Roux and Chamberland. "I think we've got it. I think we've got our vaccine. Neither the bites nor the very strong bugs did the dogs the slightest harm. The animals are absolutely immune. Now, my boys, pray and pray hard. One more task remains and we all know how important it is."

He saw understanding nods. "Yes," Émile Roux said. "We know. We've got to find out if the vaccine will protect animals *after* they've been bitten."

"Right. So pray and pray hard that it wins its race with the hydrophobia bugs. And a race it is. Will the vaccine be able to take hold in the body and protect it before the germs reach the brain?" The outcome of the race, the three men knew, was vital to the future use of the vaccine. If it won, then the very expensive process of inoculating everyone could be avoided. Unlike other vaccines, it need be employed only after the victim was exposed to the disease.

The exepriment that was now performed was ugly but

necessary. Two healthy dogs were placed in a cage together. They yelped and cowered in fear against the bars when an attendant struggled a rabid bulldog into the cage. Bloodshot eyes regarded them for a split second. Then the maddened animal charged. There was a brief flurry of brown legs and backs and the yelping became a frenzied howling. It was all over in less than a minute. The attendant pulled the bulldog from the cage. Louis hurried the first of the bitten animals to an operating board and gave him the first of fourteen hydrophobia inoculations. Émile cleansed the wounds of the second victim, but the animal received none of the protective vaccine.

The end of the story of the two dogs was seen fourteen days later. The untreated animal became ill and died. But the inoculated animal remained perfectly well, and, a month later, Louis wrote in his notebook, "He has not evidenced one symptom of hydrophobia. He is immune. The vaccine is a success."

Yes, it worked on animals—

But—

Would it now work on a human being?

The question terrified Louis. He had sought the vaccine in keeping with his promise to his three little girls to destroy sickness in mankind. Now he could not bring himself to use that vaccine for the first time on a human being. One terrible thing might happen. He knew that not all those attacked by rabid animals contracted hydrophobia. And there was no way of telling if the victim had the disease until it actually showed itself; then it was too late to use the vaccine. It was highly possible that the subject on whom he tested the protective agent might be one such person. If that were the case, the vaccine itself might give the person hydrophobia, might kill him, whereas he might live if left alone.

Should the vaccine kill, the world would condemn Louis and his discovery. His promise to Jeanne and Camille and Cécile would crash about his feet. And, worst of all, he would think himself a murderer for the rest of his days.

His quandary was worsened by hundreds of letters he received after he had reported to the Academy of Sciences and the public that a hydrophobia vaccine had been found. Parents begged him to treat their bitten children; others warned him not to play with human life. He even received a letter from the Emperor of Brazil, asking after the progress of his work and inquiring if the vaccine could soon be applied to man.

Louis closed his mind to all these letters of encouragement and protest. There was but one way to test the vaccine. He had found it. He would test it on himself. He would subject himself to the bite of a rabid dog and then inoculate himself. He would tell no one of his plans. Not Marie. Not Émile. Not Chamberland. Absolutely no one must try to stop him.

He had no chance to put his plan into action, for one morning, as he was outlining it in his notebook, Émile Roux approached his desk.

"There are three people in the next room to see you—a Monsieur Vone, and a Madame Meister and her son, Joseph."

Louis glanced up. "What do they wish?"

Émile's face was dead white. His hands were trembling. "The man and the boy have been bitten by a mad dog. The boy alone was struck fourteen times. They want you to treat them."

CHAPTER

16

The Coming of
Joseph Meister

Louis waited to hear no more. He pushed his note-book aside, hurried to the laboratory door and threw it open.

The scientist in him instantly stifled the groan that started from his lips. Directly in front of him stood the young, dark-haired Madame Meister and her nine-year-old son, Joseph. At the woman's shoulder was a heavy-set man of middle age with his arm resting in a cloth sling; this must be Theodore Vone. Madame Meister's olive-complexioned face was contorted with anxiety and her eyes were swollen from long hours of weeping. One glance at her wavering figure told Louis she was dangerously close to exhaustion and hysteria. But it was Joseph who wrenched the gasp from him. Massive bandages covered the boy's hands, arms, and face. Pain showed clearly in his wide-set, blue eyes. He stood hunched forward and held back a sob of fear at the sight of Louis.

Madame Meister broke away from her child with an eagerness that was pathetic.

"You are Monsieur Pasteur?"

"Yes."

His reply brought fresh tears to her eyes. "Thank the Lord we have found you! You must help us! Doctor Weber says you are the only man in France who can save my Joseph."

Louis steadied the woman and forced a calmness he did not really feel—and could not feel—into his voice. "Now, Madame, you must not excite yourself. I'll help you if I can. But, first, we must make the lad comfortable."

He smiled at Joseph. "Would you like to sit down?"

The boy's dark head nodded. Like so many French country children, he was slender but muscular. "Yes, Monsieur Pasteur," he replied with as much politeness as his pain would permit. He even managed a slight bow. It was an automatic gesture, one that had been demanded of him since the day he had taken his first steps.

Louis escorted the three people to chairs in front of his desk. His eyes never left Joseph. An invisible, ice-cold hand gripped his heart. Every step was wrenching agony for the boy. He gave a small, animal-like cry as he lowered himself to a chair.

"And I think my leg is bothersome," Louis told himself.

When all were seated, the scientist said, "My assistant tells me that Joseph and Monsieur Vone were bitten by a mad dog at your village in Alsace."

"Two days ago," said Madame Meister.

"It was my dog," Theodore Vone added miserably, speaking for the first time. His voice was deep, full of self-accusation.

"Tell me exactly what happened," Louis instructed gently.

"Joseph was walking to school," Madame Meister explained brokenly. "The dog ran at him from a field and knocked him down. He was too startled to fight back. All he could do was cover his face. Our village bricklayer saw what was happening from nearby. He rushed up and beat the dog off with an iron bar. But it was too late! Joseph had been bitten—oh, so many times—"

She broke off, sobbing.

Theodore Vone pushed his face forward. He whipped himself fiercely with the words, "Fourteen times, Monsieur. On the hands, the body, the face."

Louis' eyes were on his desk. He couldn't bear to look at the woman. It was a terrible story. And horribly ordinary; one that could come from every village and city across France.

He asked Vone, "When were you bitten?"

"The dog returned to my grocery store after his attack on Joseph. When I tried to chain him, he snapped at my arm. I had to kill him." His arm moved helplessly in the sling. "I would have done it years ago had I known this was going to happen. But he was a good dog."

"All of us went to Doctor Weber at Ville that night," Madame Meister said, finding her voice again. "He cauterized the wounds with carbolic, but said that Joseph and Monsieur Vone should come to you. He said you have a medicine that can save them from hydrophobia."

The words—particularly the last one—brought the woman to her feet. She leaned across the desk, her eyes wide and pleading.

"You will help us, won't you, Monsieur?"

Vone came to her side. "I don't care about myself. But,

at least, help the boy! I can't forgive myself for what's happened!"

Louis glanced quickly at Joseph and held up a warning hand. His heart was beating wildly, pouring dizzying blood into his head. Out of a clear blue sky, these people were presenting him with the opportunity for which he had searched so long, the chance of testing his vaccine on humans for the first time. But their plea crystallized all his doubts and fears of the past weeks. He must tell these people things that would be unwise for Joseph to hear.

He called to Roux. "Émile, I think Joseph would enjoy seeing one of our guinea pigs."

Understanding what Louis had in mind, Émile quickly brought one of the tiny animals to the desk and occupied Joseph's attention while Louis drew Madame Meister and Vone aside.

"My friends," he whispered intently. "Do you understand the risk you are taking—the risk you are asking me to take?"

"Risk?"

"Yes. My vaccine has worked on animals. But on human beings?" He shrugged helplessly, fearfully. "I don't know. You say Doctor Weber cauterized your wounds, Monsieur Vone, and Joseph's. Such treatment might prove sufficient to prevent the disease. And we cannot read the future. God may not intend that both of you will become sick at all. If these things are so, then we are taking a terrible chance. My vaccine might fail. It might infect you both with the disease. It might cause your—"

He could not speak the final word.

Vone said it for him.

"Our deaths?"

"Yes. And, if you have contracted hydrophobia from the bites, my vaccine might aggravate your conditions, might make your suffering all the worse." He saw Vone swallow hard. "If I caused death or greater suffering, I would be driven to insanity."

Madame Meister's face was a white mask. She was using her every last ounce of strength to speak. "And what will happen to them if they become ill without your medicine?"

Louis stared at the floor.

"You know very well what will happen," the woman went on in a vehement whisper. "They will die. Everyone of us has seen it happen before!"

Yes, they would die, like thousands of others—a slow, thirsting death.

"Please! Please, I need time to think!" He gripped Madame Meister's hands. "But, rest assured, I will try to do what is right. I promise you."

Now he turned his attention to examining the wounds of Vone and Joseph.

He sighed with relief when he saw Theodore's bared arm.

"You need not worry. You say this is the shirt you were wearing at the time of the attack? Good. See, the cloth is not even torn. It wiped away the animal's saliva. You can return home. You're quite safe from the disease."

But he paled when he saw Joseph's wounds. They were deep and ugly, particularly those on one hand, and they were beginning to swell. There seemed to be little doubt that the disease would soon afflict the nine-year-old boy.

Still, at the end of the examination, he was torn with doubt. "Madame Meister, as you may know, I am not a medical doctor. I alone cannot decide to use the vaccine. I need the advice of two physician friends."

Swiftly, he instructed his assistants, "Émile, find Doctors Grancher and Vulpian at once. Tell them to come here at five this afternoon to examine Joseph. Chamberland, see that Madame Meister and Joseph get some rest after their long journey. They need it badly. Ask the head of Rollin College if they may have a room there for the day."

After everyone had departed, Louis made his way to the Academy of Sciences. But he paid no attention to the learned discussion that, at the beginning of this day, he had looked forward to hearing. His mind had room only for the terrible choice he knew he must soon make.

Free the world from a deadly evil.

Or risk giving a child a disease or, at the very least, risk intensifying his agony if the disease was already present.

He could only hope that Grancher and Vulpian would make his decision a little easier.

At last five o'clock came. As the yellow-red July sun dropped below Paris rooftops and the sound of evening traffic came through the lab windows from the street below, Doctors Grancher and Vulpian examined Joseph's wounds. Tensely, Louis sat at his desk. His fingers, drumming the cluttered desk top, became the focal point of all his nervousness, all his fright.

The faces of the physicians were troubled when at last they turned to him. Vulpian, a member of the Rabies Commission, was the first to speak when they had drawn him to a far corner of the room. "The wounds are festering, Louis. Doctor Weber cauterized them—but twelve hours after the attack. I think he did no good at all. In my opinion, the lad cannot escape hydrophobia."

Louis stared hard at Vulpian. His respect for this reserved professor was great. "You are certain?"

"As certain as it is humanly possible to be at this moment."

"Then you think I should use the vaccine?"

"Yes. And the sooner the better."

Grancher saw doubt still torturing the scientist's face. "You must use it. There is no other treatment available."

"Your experiments with animals have been so successful that we think it will work with humans. This is what you've wanted," Vulpian said. "This is your chance to learn if it works. Take it!"

Louis ran his hand through his hair. "But do I have the right to take it? Suppose it worsens his condition instead of curing him?"

"Louis!" Vulpian's ordinarily quiet tone was sharp. "Without the vaccine, he will surely die. Will you then be able to live with yourself, knowing you could have helped but did not? It is not only your right to use it—it is your duty!"

Duty?

That word seemed to have a magical effect on Louis. Vulpian was right. He had prayed to God for guidance as to how to test the vaccine on humans. Perhaps little Joseph Meister was God's answer. If so, it was his duty to turn to the vaccine and to place all his trust in God.

Quite suddenly, all indecision left him.

His excited voice filled the laboratory.

"Roux! Chamberland! We'll prepare the vaccine!"

The Final Victory

The first injection was made early that evening. Just a few drops of a liquid containing fragments of the medulla oblongata of a rabbit infected with hydrophobia—they were all that were needed. Roux and Chamberland passed the fluid into a Pravaz syringe while Louis spoke with Madame Meister.

"I want you to know exactly what we are going to do. Joseph will receive an injection each day for the next fourteen days. For the first injection, we have chosen very weak germs. Each day, stronger ones will be used, thereby increasing Joseph's resistance to the disease. On the very last day, he will receive quite a powerful injection. But by that time, if all goes well, he should be completely immune to the illness."

If all goes well . . .

Madame Meister studied his lined face closely. She saw there, so clearly, all the torment in his mind. For the first time that day, she smiled. She touched his arm, almost shyly.

"Monsieur Pasteur, please understand that I trust you completely. I know you are going to do your best. Even if the worst happens, I shall not blame you."

Louis' reply was barely audible.

"Thank you."

He turned now from mother to son. Joseph Meister became the hub of a circle of tense, pale adults. Grancher and Vulpian might have been statues, so silent and motionless were they as they watched the scientist crouch before the boy. Roux moved quietly to Louis' side, a lamp in his hand. Madame Meister stood inches from her child's back, her hands gripping his shoulders, gently but firmly, as if some of her strength and some of her faith in Pasteur could pass through her fingers into the slender, pain-wracked body. The lamplight reached her face and Louis saw that her lips were moving in silent prayer. Outside, the sound of passing traffic was muted. Louis had the odd feeling that a Paris that did not know what was happening at this moment in the lab had become deathly still.

He spoke quietly to Joseph. "I'm going to vaccinate your side. It will take but a few seconds."

He saw the boy's eyes flick to Chamberland who now approached with the syringe. Those eyes, luminous and almost black in the lamplight, were widened with fear. A sob broke from the child. He was certain he faced a painful ordeal. He had had enough pain for a lifetime in the past two days.

"Now, Joseph, I'm going to make you a promise," Louis said. "I'm not going to hurt you one bit."

The boy stared at him suspiciously.

"Promise?"

"It is a promise. If I hurt you at all, you may have for your very own the guinea pig Monsieur Roux showed you today."

"Is that a promise, too?"

"It is," Louis answered solemnly. "You must remain absolutely still and help me as much as you can."

"All right."

Joseph's teeth caught his lower lip. He fought hard to hold back his sobs. The guinea pig—that was something worth trying for.

Louis took the syringe from Chamberland and held it to the light to check the sharpness of its point. He was surprised to find his hand so steady.

Now he lowered the needle point to Joseph's thigh. He hesitated. A burning liquid rose momentarily behind his eyes. He knew full well this was the split second toward which he had worked so long; the split second in which his promise to Jeanne and Camille and Cécile might at last be fulfilled. This split second might see him send disease retreating from a human being for the first time in his life. The needle went a fraction of an inch beneath Joseph's skin. The boy gasped and in Louis' mind was the vision of invisible giants stealing into the child's body.

Giants that could bring health and make a wondrous thing of his promise to his little girls.

Or . . .

But he must not think of that other horror. He had placed his trust in God and he had tried to fulfill his promise. He must believe that he had done the right thing.

"There," he said, "it is done. It wasn't so bad after all, was it?"

Joseph admitted slowly. "No. I hardly felt it at all." Then, more quickly, "But I can still have the guinea pig, can't I?"

The boy's question shattered the tension. A slight gust of laughter filled the room, but the faces, Louis saw, were still pale, still tight with strain. Vulpian gripped his hand and said softly:

"A wonderful thing has been done here tonight."

Louis gazed down at Joseph Meister's head.

"I wonder. We shall soon know."

Again in his life Louis had to live through a torturous period of waiting. Each morning, he expected to find Joseph stricken with hydrophobia, Joseph calling for water he could not drink, Joseph tossing feverishly on his bed and crying in the tightening grip of death. But, each morning, he found the boy in fine health. The injections continued and the wounds began to heal.

Still, watching the boy at play with the animals in the lab, Louis could not bring himself to hope that the vaccine had proved successful. The illnesss could steal upon the child at any moment. Louis smiled grimly to himself and remarked, "And I thought the waiting for the Pouilly-le-Fort results was bad. It was nothing compared to this!"

But Joseph continued to flourish as the day for the final injection approached. This was to be the strongest of the lot and Louis found sleep impossible the night before it must be administered. Not a room in his house was free from his nervous, restless pacing. Marie gave up all hope of retiring and stayed at his side, brewing him cups of strong coffee and murmuring words of encouragement, until the dark hours just before dawn when at last his eyes closed in fitful slumber as he sat at the kitchen table.

"Remember," she had told him many times that night, "that you think this boy was heaven sent."

It was hard to keep those words in mind as he made the final injection. So many other thoughts, all fearful, constantly drove them from view. Joseph Meister was now as much in his heart as his own son. For every remaining day of his life he would remember so many things about the boy—his laughter, his curiosity, his love of the animals in the lab. On one occasion, he recalled, Joseph had found Roux and Chamberland about to inoculate a test animal with a deadly serum. "How he begged them to spare the life of that small creature," he reminisced aloud. "And how quickly I called off the experiment! Nothing must happen to this boy. He *must* remain well. We've come so far. Let us go the rest of the way without tragedy!"

The final days of waiting dragged by and the final nights of sleeplessness with them. Joseph showed not a sign of illness. Hope began to flower in Louis' mind and grew stronger with each passing hour. It was now hope that not only would Joseph live, but that the whole world would soon live free of the terror of hydrophobia.

At last it was mid-August of 1885. It was a time of heat for Paris and a time of relief and happiness for Louis. Now, after all the weeks of doubt and worry, he could write of that cherished freedom. "Joseph is yet well and seems recovered from his wounds. It has been thirty-one days since he was bitten. *He is now quite safe. The vaccine is successful.*"

How proud those brief sentences made him. Had he done nothing in life but this, he would have considered himself the most fortunate of men. And, now that they were written and Joseph Meister was on his way back home to a healthy life, how tired he felt. Rest and sleep and quiet talk with Marie were the things he wanted now. The pen slipped from bloodless fingers and he looked at it with a wry smile. "Louis, I'm afraid you're getting too old for your own good."

But rest was not to be his. The news of what he had done swept over the world like a fresh, vitalizing wind at the end of a humid summer day. People everywhere rejoiced. Pasteur had done it again! Was there no end to his miracles? Anthrax. Chicken cholera. The diseases of wines and silk-worms. The doctrine of spontaneous generation. Surgery without sterilization. Bad fermentations. Each and every one of them had met their destruction at the hands of this bearded, eccentric, little Frenchman. And now hydrophobia was taking its rightful place on the block!

No, there would be no rest and no sleep and no quiet talk with Marie, for, from all parts of the world, frightened parents were to flock to his lab with their children who had been bitten by rabid dogs and wolves. Often the laboratory lights were to burn all through the night as exhausted assistants worked frantically to prepare enough vaccine to keep abreast of the demand.

A case as urgent as that of Joseph Meister was brought to Louis. A fourteen-year-old shepherd boy, J. B. Juprille, had been bitten by a mad dog while bravely protecting his small companions from attack. Treatment began seven days after the incident. Had the boy come too late to be saved? No. Not at all. The inoculations were entirely successful.

The *New York Herald* raised money through public subscription to send four bitten children of American workmen to Paris. The youngest of the group was a boy of five. Like Joseph, he was frightened at the sight of Louis' syringe. His fright changed to surprise at the very slight prick of the needle and he laughed. "Is this all we have come such a long journey for?" The children returned to their homeland in the best of health.

One incident, however, marred Louis' complete happiness at this time. On November 9, ten-year-old Louise Pelletier was brought to him. She had been bitten in early October, thirty-seven days before. The sight of her broke his heart. The case was hopeless. The wounds were festering and hydrophobia would show itself at any moment. It was much, much too late for the preventive treatment to take any real effect. Still, he must try. He couldn't send the child away to certain death without making some effort. After all, a miracle might happen.

But a miracle did not happen. Louise received her inoculations and returned to school. For a while, she seemed on her way back to health. Then suddenly the disease gripped her. Louis rushed to her house. He tried new inoculations, but without success. He could only sit at her bedside and hold her hand and hear her cry out the wish that he not leave the room. He was with her when she died. He stood up very slowly and very tiredly and walked downstairs to face the little girl's parents. Tears were streaming from his eyes when he told them, "I did so wish I could have saved your little one."

But tiny Louise was his only failure. He was able to tell the Academy of Sciences and the many physicians and scientists who visited his lab from every country in Europe that, out of three hundred and fifty people treated in just a few weeks, only she had met death.

From Smolensk, Russia, came nineteen peasants who had

been attacked by a mad wolf three weeks before. All Paris held its breath as Louis treated these strangely dressed people who could not understand one word he said. He was almost certain that too much time had elapsed for the vaccine to be of any help. But, as in the case of Louise, he could not turn them away. He gave them two shots daily to make up for the lost time. Miraculously, the vaccine saved all but three lives.

Paris—all France—went wild with pride in Louis.

Nothing was too good for him. In the first rush of people seeking vaccinations, he had voiced the old, old wish for a proper laboratory in which to carry on his work. All right, a grateful public replied upon learning that the Academy of Sciences had appointed a commission to plan such a lab, you shall have the finest possible, finer and even more magnificent than you can imagine. They kept their promise by flooding him with donations from all over the world.

These contributions, from rich and poor alike, from noblemen and peasants, from factory workers and farmers, artists and merchants, built for him something that was far more than just a laboratory. It was a monument to a lifetime spent questing after the unknown; to a lifetime spent holding up before the world the momentous fact that invisible, infinitesimal life can destroy or serve mankind; to a lifetime spent fighting sickness and winning over one of the most dreaded afflictions known to man. They built for him the Pasteur Institute, dedicated to the treatment of hydrophobia and the battle against all disease. To this day it remains one of the greatest centers of scientific research in the world.

One night Marie came down from their bedroom to find

Louis at his desk in his study. It was long past the hour at which he usually retired, but she found him wide awake, his head inclined over a long sheet of paper. When he looked up, she saw that, though there were tears standing in the corners of his eyes, he was smiling.

"My dear, you must see this," he said and held out the paper to her. She accepted it and saw that it was filled with row upon row of names, and she heard her husband explain happily, "All those names belong to the people of Alsace. They have contributed forty-three thousand francs to the building of the Institute. And see this . . ."

His hand, which seemed to her to be little more than bone, touched a name far down the list. Here, she knew, was the reason for the tears glistening in the corners of her husband's eyes.

The name he indicated was that of Joseph Meister.

She smiled and felt a peculiar little tightness deep in her throat. "I'm very proud of you, Louis. And so happy that your dream is coming true—that at last you're going to have a fine laboratory of your own."

She was surprised to see him shake his head. His expression was suddenly quiet and thoughtful, and the lamplight revealed how deep the lines of age and tiredness were in his face. "I've been thinking, Marie. The lab doesn't really belong to me alone," he said. His voice was no longer the strong voice of the young man she had married so many years ago. It was now little more than a hoarse whisper. "It belongs to scientists everywhere. It's a sign to them that the day is dawning when they shall no longer have to work in the meanest of quarters. The day is at hand when they shall be given the equipment and the space they need and deserve. And what a day it is, my dear. It's going to bring new discoveries. It's going to bring man a greater health and a longer life than he has ever realized possible. I'm so happy I've lived to see it dawn."

His hand closed over her's. "Oh, Marie, there's so much I want to do. I've kept my promise to little Jeanne and Camille and Cécile. But I want to keep it over and over again. There's so much sickness that I want to find and fight . . ."

"You'll have your chance to fight it, my dear. I know you will," she whispered, and then made her voice very light and very practical. "But not tonight. Tonight—right this very minute—you're going to bed and to sleep. Now come along, Professor Pasteur. I'll not put up with any sort of argument."

As they ascended the stairs together, holding hands as if they were two children, she knew he would never again keep his promise to his little girls. She knew that which she had not dared to tell him in the room below—that his days of fighting the invisible and the terrifying were over. The years of endless labor had robbed him of his vitality and physical health. The fact was painfully evident in his every leaden step, in the slump of his shoulders, in the hoarseness of his voice and the coldness of his touch and the paleness of his face. It was time for him to step aside and let others carry on his work. It was time for him to hand the torch of leadership to younger men and be content to see them forge ahead of him, deeper and deeper into the uncharted, dark regions of scientific research.

It was time for him to rest.

And he could rest with a quiet, satisfied mind, for he had completed his mission in life.

He had left no doubt in the mind of the world of the

breathtaking power of minute life forms it could not see.

He—and a handful of others—had forged a wide trail along which all the biological and medical sciences would pass in all the years to come.

The Last Days

Louis, though he could never bring himself to admit it openly, also realized his days of exhausting labor were done.

Though his mind continued to visualize vast new fields to conquer, he found his health not up to the rigors of earlier times, and he had to pass many of his ideas on to younger men. It thrilled him to see them at work, building their own careers and widening the horizons of scientific research. Yet it hurt to be unable to labor at their sides. But really, he told himself, he had no cause for complaint. He counted up the years. He was close to seventy. He had been given a long and fruitful life. It was only right and fitting that he should surrender his place at the microscope to the young and give them their chance for accomplishment and fame.

But his late sixties were joyful years for him. He saw the completion of the Pasteur Institute; he would have been doubly happy had he known that, in a future year, the loyal Émile Roux would be installed as director of the Institute.

The scientist's days were filled with many touching

honors. The Governor General of Algiers wrote him to say that the name of Pasteur had been given to a village in Algiers. A number of streets in French cities and a district in Canada were named after him.

Of all the tributes, the finest was paid him on his seventieth birthday, December 27, 1892. A national holiday was declared and a giant celebration, attended by scientists and dignitaries from over the world, was held in his honor in the auditorium of the Sorbonne.

Bent and gray-haired, the scientist leaned on the arm of the President of the Republic as he entered the hall. A band struck up a triumphal march. Louis gazed round the vast auditorium and suddenly tears were in his eyes. He had never seen so many people gathered in one spot in all his life—and they were all here because of him. Up on the stage were the Ambassadors from England, Austria-Hungary, Russia, Denmark, Holland, Sweden, Norway, and Bavaria. Seated alongside them were representatives from the Academy of Sciences, the École Normale, the Academy of Medicine, and a dozen or more other scientific societies in France and in foreign nations.

Louis moved slowly down the aisle to the brightly lighted and decorated stage. He glimpsed a hundred familiar faces: faces belonging to the best laboratory minds in Europe—Burdon, Sanderson, Lankester, and Haskovek. Some of the faces were those of old friends. Others belonged to one-time adversaries. In these latter countenances, he glimpsed not a sign of the angers of the past.

Through a mist of tears, he looked to the galleries. Up there were the young men of the Sorbonne and the École Normale, the teachers and scientists of the future.

Someone rose in front of him. A smile crossed his face and he stretched out his arms. It was Joseph Lister, who, so many years ago, felt as Louis did about cleanliness in hospitals and, out of that feeling, made surgery safe for all. The two men embraced like brothers.

Louis took his place on the stage amidst deafening applause. A large engraved medal was presented to him and then he heard the voice of Joseph Lister, who had been chosen as the representative of the Royal Societies of London and Edinburgh, ring out over the audience:

"M. Pasteur," the voice was saying, "the great honor has been accorded me of bringing you the homage of the sciences of medicine and surgery. As a matter of fact, there is no one living in the entire world to whom the medical sciences owe so much as they do to you. . . . You have lifted the veil which for centuries had overhung infectious diseases. You have discovered and demonstrated their microbic nature. . . . You can therefore well understand that the sciences of medicine and surgery are eager upon this solemn occasion to offer you the profound homage of admiration and gratitude."

Then it was time for Louis to speak. But his broken health had made him so feeble that he was forced to have his son deliver his address for him. Jean-Baptiste held his shoulders straight and his voice was strong and clear as he spoke the words that were to echo down through the corridors of science for years to come:

"Gentlemen. . . . You bring me the deepest joy that a man can experience, who believes invincibly that science and peace will triumph over ignorance and war; that peoples will come to a common understanding, not to destroy but to build, and that the future will belong to those who will have done most for suffering humanity. . . ."

Jean-Baptiste lifted his face to the galleries and sent his father's words winging upwards. "Young men, have confidence in that sure and powerful method of which we do not yet know the fundamental secrets. . . . Live in the serene peace of laboratories and libraries. Say to yourselves first of all: what have I done for my instruction? and as you go on further, what have I done for my country? until the time comes when you may have the immense happiness of thinking you have contributed in some way to the progress and welfare of humanity."

That great day of honor and celebration marked Louis' almost total retirement from public life. The remainder of the span of life that had been allotted to him was spent in quiet research at the Pasteur Institute and in speaking of and defending his many discoveries and theories.

Much of his time was passed at his beloved village of Arbois and at his branch laboratory in the beautiful park of Villeneuve l'Étang, near St. Cloud.

He lived and worked and rested in peace. Life was drawing to a close and he was fully aware of it. The paralysis that had afflicted him so many years ago returned and made speech almost impossible for him. Then, at last, his health failed him completely and he was forced to retire to the bed from which he would never again rise.

But he did so without complaint. Friends came from over the face of France to sit at his bedside and cheer his last hours. And there was Marie. She was always at his side, reading to him from his favorite book, *The Life of St. Vin-*

cent de Paul. Dreamily, hearing her quiet voice, he hoped his own work had brought as much good to the children of the world as had the labors of the humble, gentle Vincent. He felt he could listen to Marie read forever.

With the life of Vincent strong in his mind and one hand gripping a crucifix while the other caressed Marie's fingers, Louis closed his eyes for the last time at 4:40 in the afternoon of September 28, 1895. The mind that had worked such wonders for the science and health of the world was still at last. Louis Pasteur was dead at seventy-three.

His body was placed in a chapel in the Pasteur Institute at the request of the French government. On the marble walls of the chapel were engraved the names of the fields Louis investigated—fields that bear witness to the awesome power of microbic life in our world:

—Crystalline Structures
—Fermentation
—Spontaneous Generation
—Diseases of the Wines
—Diseases of the Silkworms
—Causes of Contagious Diseases
—Curative Vaccines
—Hydrophobia

Four carved angels watch over his tomb. They are Faith, Hope, Charity, and Science. He rests beneath them today while the work he began and inspired continues in every laboratory of the Pasteur Institute.